BIOSOCIAL FACTORS IN
MENTAL ILLNESS

Publication Number 519
AMERICAN LECTURE SERIES®

A Monograph in
AMERICAN LECTURES IN CLINICAL PSYCHIATRY

Edited by
HOWARD P. ROME, M.D.
Mayo Clinic
Rochester, Minnesota

BIOSOCIAL FACTORS
IN
MENTAL ILLNESS

By

JAMES K. FEIBLEMAN

Department of Philosophy
Tulane University
and
Department of Psychiatry
School of Medicine
Louisiana State University

With an Introduction by

MARVIN K. OPLER

Department of Psychiatry
University of Buffalo School of Medicine
and
Department of Sociology
University of Buffalo

CHARLES C THOMAS · PUBLISHER
Springfield · Illinois · U. S. A.

CHARLES C THOMAS • PUBLISHER

BANNERSTONE HOUSE

301–327 East Lawrence Avenue, Springfield, Illinois, U. S. A.

*With THOMAS BOOKS careful attention is given to all details of
manufacturing and design. It is the Publisher's desire to present books
that are satisfactory as to their physical qualities and artistic possibilities
and appropriate for their particular use. THOMAS BOOKS will be true
to those laws of quality that assure a good name and good will.*

Printed in the United States of America

INTRODUCTION

MARVIN K. OPLER

PHILOSOPHY, of course, pivots today on a wide arc of scientific findings performing a task of synthesis and interpretation. There is no reason why the philosopher, if he takes a philosophy of science seriously, cannot himself conduct research. But perhaps it is well for us that leading philosophers have reserved the privilege that a naturalist like Aristotle innovated, of providing the over-view, the scrutiny of meaningful areas between disciplines, and at times the challenge to loose semantics of persons writing in a given field of science. This too is research—scholarly research.

Professor Feibleman, with an eye trained on both scientific findings and their wider interpretations, offers just such an over-view, critical scrutiny and corrective for myopic workers in behavioral sciences. That he has chosen a field both close to scientific ethics and the concerns of students of social pathology is all the better; for the philosopher of science has tended to hew too closely to "physical" sciences and ontological problems than to more mundane human affairs that concern the anthropologist, the psychiatrist or psychologist, the sociologist, and which contain the behavioral dimensions that bedevil us all.

It is pleasing, personally, to find Professor Feibleman inveighing first against "the closed psycho-somatic system" in much the same terms as von Bertalanffy or the writer of his Introduction in *Culture, Psychiatry and Human Values* (1956) or in *The Symposium of Social and Preventive Psychiatry* published by the Walter Reed Institute of Research in 1958. This is undoubtedly the realistic starting point and it is appropriate that a philosopher,

v

concerned with more than one "field" of science, should note this false start of those insisting on closure first of all. When Professor Feibleman hastens to add that behavior in isolation from other integrative levels is not a proper subject-matter for study, one thinks of the decades of waste motion spent in symptomatic classifications of mental illness (Kraepelin) divorced from sociocultural setting; or of the forced isolation of the human beings themselves giving rise to hospitalism and its syndromes; or finally of the divisiveness of neurophysiologic, biochemical, or in erstwhile years, "constitutional" approaches to illness, which as Seymour Kety has recently pointed out, failed to control even such intrusive variables as the schizophrenics coffee "habit" while ignoring more crucial sociocultural components and determinants entirely. As suggested, weighting the levels of integration in sociocultural, psychological and biologic sciences leads to what Einstein typified as "asking the right questions." Is science, then, not really what the scientist does, in a particular day and age, and in his more self-conscious movements? The preconscious gifts of imagination and the thrill of discovery have themselves such limitations of possibilities imposed upon them.

Some may argue that Professor Feibleman has himself closed the system at certain points, but they cannot deny that he has been provocative, original and challenging in posing novel hypotheses for testing.

FOREWORD

THE aim of this monograph is to study the relations between mental illness and human culture. There have been many studies of mental illness in various other cultures. But the effect of culture as such is more fundamental than the accultural stress brought about by the conflicts between cultures or by the imposition or encroachment of one culture on another.

Thanks to science we know a great deal about the physical world and the biological organism but as yet far too little about society. It might help to begin at the beginning; to use the recent findings and speculations in neurophysiology to explore the effects of culture on the individual. For it is now well known that cultural factors play an important part both in the social psychology and even in the psychopathology of the individual.

The members of society interact continually with artifacts, the material objects which have been altered through human agency by which they are surrounded. The cumulative effect of such interaction is to increase the complexity of human culture, and also that of the neural pathways. But there is a vast difference in the rate by which these two processes take place. The first can be measured in thousands of years, the second only in millions. Cultures rise and fall in a matter of millennia, whereas vast epochs are required for a change in the capacity of the human skull. Alterations in civilization occur quickly; they occur in neurophysiological structures far more slowly.

It is to be expected, then, that the swift pace of culture, with which the development of the nervous system can hardly keep up, should produce strains and dislocations. This is the process named by Hughlings Jackson dissolution, the opposite of evolution, and a name to cover the mental diseases: the neuroses and psychoses.

In the final chapters an effort is made to put together some available techniques in order to construct a new therapy. The models are those of Chinese "brainwashing" (or of forced religious conversion), the programming of computers, and electroshock (insulin coma or metrazol convulsions). The resultant therapy consists in the attempt to imprint mental patients with an acceptable schedule of ideas under nociceptive stimulation.

Grateful acknowledgment is hereby made to the editors of the following journals for permission to reprint articles which first appeared in their pages: to the *American Journal of Psychiatry* for "Ecological Factors in Human Maladaptation"; to *The International Journal of Social Psychiatry* for "Biosocial Adaptation and Mental Illness"; to *The Journal of Nervous and Mental Disease* for "The Cultural Circuit in Psychology and Psychiatry"; to *The Journal of Psychology* for "Transfer Matching: A New Method in Psychotherapy," and "The Stressed Conditioning of Psychotics"; and to *The Psychological Record* for "An Illustration of Retention Schemata." "Behavior as Response" was read before the American Psychiatric Association Regional Research Conference held in New Orleans on January 14, 1960, and has appeared in *Problems in Communication* (Psychiatric Research Reports No. 14).

J.K.F.

CONTENTS

BIOSOCIAL FACTORS IN MENTAL ILLNESS

CHAPTER 1

BEHAVIOR AS RESPONSE *

T HE following argument will undertake to show that an object-oriented psychology is possible. The subject is stimulated by objects and makes its response in action on objects. This shifts the center of emphasis from the organism alone to the organism plus that segment of the environment with which it interacts, and from learning to belief and the will, concepts which have been out of fashion in psychology. The communication channels are the same as the interaction channels: from material object to organism and back to material object. To show this we shall have to make a discursus into some older frameworks.

1

The experimental sciences do not operate entirely in a vacuum or altogether with the deadly precision with which they have been credited. To a larger extent than has been understood, the background of abstract ideas has exerted its influence. This has been a help at times but just as often a hindrance. Speculative atomism was a help; after several millennia it led to the development in physics of the atomic theory (19, p. 38) and finally to quantum mechanics. But on the other hand the Cartesian distinction between conscious "mind" and "matter" which replaced the Aristotelian categories of "form" and "matter" has been paralyzing to

* "Behavior as Response" was read before the American Psychiatric Association Regional Research Conference held in New Orleans on January 14, 1960, and has appeared in *Problems in Communication* (Psychiatric Research Reports #14).

3

the sciences of psychology (13). For it has meant that the mind of man has been considered in isolation from the matter of the external world, leaving the only matter to be considered that of the body (20). Under these self-imposed theoretical limitations, both mind and matter are squeezed into the somatic organism, and the only stimulation the mind can receive is from the body. "Stimulus-and-response" are conceived as "body and mind."

There are reasons for suspecting that such a confinement is impoverishing (14, 28). Trains of nerve-impulses initiated at the peripheral end-organs are all alike (1, p. 21), and we should never be able to account for the differences in patterns between them without reference to stimuli in the external world. One consequence has been the conception of the psychological sciences as functions of human behavior. In the constricted circuit, the only response the mind can make is to the body; but this train of nerve-impulses ends, so far as psychology is concerned, where the stimulus began, namely, at the peripheral end-organs.

The closed psycho-somatic system constitutes a false isolate in terms of the integrative levels of the empirical sciences. We have come to learn not only that "man" is the name for an organization with subdivisions at many levels: physical, chemical, biological, psychological and cultural, but that his interactions with his environment occur also in terms of these same levels. A new conception of stimulus and response is needed, one which takes into consideration the role of the external world. The external world contains physical objects, chemical elements, biological organisms and other minds, any of which may interact with the human subject under investigation. Finally, it can be supposed that the subjective response is a function of the objective stimulus, on the ground that the world existed before the individual and so conditions him, though not, as we shall see, without being affected by the interchange.

One variety of progress in science consists in the discovery of problems in areas that were not even known to exist (15). In the physical sciences, such problems are now centered around quantum phenomena. In the behavioral sciences, the area of special interest is the frontier where psychology marches with neurophysiology.

In the domain of neurophysiology, new discoveries—for example the work of Magoun and others on the reticular formation of the brain stem (12)—have disclosed new and exciting problems, as is customary in the experimental sciences. The difficulties in the way of a successful understanding of the central nervous system are stupendous and paralyzing. The complexity of cortical structures, for instance, probably exceeds the power of existing instruments of analysis. Cleavage between the physical sciences and the behavioral sciences lies in just this analysis of the central nervous system. Involved in the propagation of a nerve impulse, for instance, there are electrical, mechanical and chemical changes. Each of these can be analyzed and interpreted from a different point of view.

The substitution of the more complex integrative levels for the mind-body distinction does away with the attempt to reduce the mental to the physical. Through reference to the integrative levels, it becomes clear that there has been a confusion of *manipulation* with *degradation*. For instance, human behavior can be manipulated to some extent by means of biochemicals. But this does not mean that the psychological level can be degraded to the neurophysiological. There exists an authentic psychological level and probably a number of intervening sublevels. For even though the control mechanism of the human individual is the central nervous system, there is a great deal more to the human individual as a whole than can be studied in terms of a single organ no matter how high its function or how intricate its ramifications. If it is the case, as Bohm (3, pp. 37, 50–1, 60, 122, 125) has suggested, that effects lie always at one integrative level higher than their causes, then what the psychologist has been studying in his analysis of behavior are simply the macroscopic and overt results of microscopic and covert neurophysiological causes. But there is more to the situation than his findings would indicate. For at the psychological level there are autonomous and indigenous organizing relations and qualitative principles to be found. Then, too, the stimuli are not only nor chiefly initiated from within the organism.

As we shall see with increasing relevance when we come to examine the psychological effects of the integrative levels of culture, behavior does not take place in a vacuum but is always about some material thing, and in the interaction between tool, say, and organism the effect upon the behavior of the organism is to be located. Hence behavior in isolation, as in the behavior of human individuals, cannot be regarded by the investigator as a proper subject-matter for study.

Thus whether mental events can or cannot be reduced to physical events does not depend entirely upon the further development of neurophysiology. We do need to know a great deal more about the cerebral cortex. But even so, there is the distinction between the internal and the external worlds to be accounted for. There are relations to be studied between the psychological individual and his cultural environment. There are variations from individual to individual and variations, too, in the effects exerted upon him by the environment; but there are always individuals and always effects. To borrow an analogy, the camera is a physical instrument, and the details concerning its operation are well known; but nobody knows just what pictures will be taken with it, only that there will be pictures and that the pictures will be physical pictures. If it were possible to show the causal or occasional relation between the cortex and awareness, the investigator still would not know just what external relations or external qualities would be apprehended by awareness or what effects they would produce in the individual.

The strong interest in the analogy between the computer and the human brain lies in the information it suggests concerning the operation of one kind of mental process, namely, deduction. In the so-called field of cybernetics it has proved useful to suppose that the higher nervous system operates much like a feedback mechanism, so that when anything occurs that might constitute a disturbance, messages are transmitted through the nervous network to the brain, stimulating responses which initiate actions intended to restore the equilibrium. Thus the circuit constitutes a kind of regulative system responsible for the maintenance of the organism at a certain level. Abstraction allegedly results from the closing of the neural network and the consequent reverberations of the message (11, pp. 40, 47, 54). Deduction is only another word for calculation, and so the operation of an electronic computer is only a very crude and very fast model of one side of the thinking mechanism.

Recent studies make it appear that while abstract thought takes place in the frontal lobe, both speech and consciousness are closely connected with the diencephalon, while sensory and motor centers are more widespread. Excision and stimulation experiments have suggested broad lines of association but have not eliminated the difficulties in the way of checking results. When the hypothesis concerning the relation of levels of cause to effect is applied here, it becomes obvious that an increasing array of substantial forms remains to be uncovered at what is still an undisclosed number of integrative sublevels. If so, then the doctrine of levels will have to be redesigned and reevaluated for this purpose. The qualitative justification for a division of the levels could be made elsewhere, perhaps with limits both well below and well above consciousness: namely, by organic life and by the social ethos respectively.

That the integrative levels are known to exist within the human individual is made evident by the diversity of psychological schools. Introspective psychology, behaviorism, *gestalt* psychology, psychoanalysis, all assuming that they are producing conflicting theories with respect to the same subject-matter, and that one of them must be right and the others wrong, have been in conflict for some time. Yet a careful consideration of the psychological field would reveal that they are not talking about the same level. For the psychological field, like the chemical and the biological, for instance, has many sublevels and the various schools of psychology which represent them need produce no genuine conflict among themselves. *Gestalt* psychology, for example, addresses itself to consciousness; behaviorism to overt action; psychoanalysis to the pathology of the unconscious; and so on. Far from having to decide which psychological school is the correct one, perhaps we ought to look for more schools to occupy the gaps. Some extensions have already proved useful; as, for instance, Piaget's work on the mental development of the child (18), and the work of Lorenz and Tinbergen in animal psychology (24).

Nevertheless, it is certain that invariants do exist and await in-

quiry at levels ranging all the way from the raw material of behavior to the dynamics of motivation. From the stimulus-response
systems of behavior to the frustration-aggression studies of motivation, from the clinical studies of individuals to the massing of
group data, there are invariants of many degrees of worth dis-
coverable among the rates of change. But they do not all divide
between neurophysiology on the one hand, and social psychology
on the other. For at times it appears that social psychology (to
the pathology of which psychiatry belongs) reaches down as far
as neurophysiology, that, in short, the social behavior manifests
itself within the human individual at unconscious levels and that
the organism is more complex and less isolable than has been
supposed.

Be that as it may, the defenders of the traditional psychology
currently maintain that the proper subject-matter of psychology is
the behavior of animals, and if we interpret this to include everything that the behavior is about, they may be correct in their con-
tention. The enormous importance of abnormalities of behavior
at the human level has for obvious practical purposes outweighed
many other considerations, and hence pathological psychology
has been given a prominent place among the psychological sciences. Clinical and laboratory researches have led to many surprising results in this field, and much more remains to be done.
In other areas the relations between social psychology and the
structure of the unconscious seem most promising. Much help
will of course come from the recent rapid advances in neurophysiology (5), though it is too early yet to estimate their effect
upon psychology proper. In social psychology, which lies at the
upper level of the psychological sciences, liaison will have to be
made with the lowest of the social sciences.

The subject-matter of human psychology would seem to be the
behavior of human individuals. Below mental events lies the area
of neurophysiology, while above individual human behavior lies
social behavior. Social psychology would seem to be the lowest
level of the cultural or anthropological level rather than the upper
level of the psychological. This may prove to be an arbitrary distinction when we consider that it does not matter where we divide the empirical psychological domain so long as the division is

marked by a quality, and there are qualities here lying very close together.

A weakness implicit in the position of behaviorism is that while other empirical levels consist in entities as well as processes, psychology can claim only a process: that of behavior. Is the activity of the single individual animal the psychological entity? But is the single individual—say for example a human individual—a valid isolate at all? Perhaps it would be better to describe the subject-matter of psychology as the control mechanism of the human individual. If so, we are on dangerous ground again and will have to define very carefully how this control mechanism is triggered and how in this way it extends beyond the nervous system.

The development of a theory of the cultural circuit may hold a clue to the solution of this problem. For a linear process denotes an activity merely, whereas a circuit may disclose the structure of an entity. And here psychopathology can help too. Psychopathology is situational psychology. It is the strongest evidence for the existence of a level of individual psychology; for where there is a pathology there must be a norm from which a departure has been made. There must be a healthy mental state with respect to the cultural environment, and its investigation could be one of the tasks of psychology proper. It is not possible to develop a theory of osteology from a study of broken bones; but from a study of broken bones it would be possible to infer that the normal bone is an unbroken one and so arrive at the notion that there could be a theory of osteology. Personality studies are evidence that there is a conception of the normal human individual. "Personality" has replaced what the Greeks once called "character," which carries with it more of the denotation of structural strength.

If the rule of the integrative levels is correct, namely, that diversity is increased upward in the levels, then by the time the investigator reaches the psychological level, it could be expected to be enormous. The proper isolate for analysis at the psychological level is the cultural circuit, which includes together with the human individual the segment of the environment with which he interacts. This segment could include other human individuals with their language, the material objects of culture, or in all likelihood both. Ego and artifact are not on the same level of analysis (9), but for purposes of investigation they may be considered the integral parts of a single isolable system. In any case, the complexity is large and will have to be reckoned with. At the higher integrative levels, while it is true that the diversity increases rapidly, still the similarities though small remain, and because they are small are crucial. And it is with the similarities and not with the differences that science is primarily concerned. In this connection, the presence of enormous diversity is a signal that the uniformities will be complex affairs and difficult to ascertain, not that they will not exist.

Existence is everywhere dense, and the tools employed to probe it at any level are always somewhat less complex than the element chosen for analysis. This is the reason given by von Neumann and others for the failure thus far of the efforts to analyze the human brain. Even the computer, which in some ways is the most complex machine yet devised, falls short of the complexity of the brain, judged by the artificial componentry of the machine and the natural one of the brain, by a factor of some 10^8 or 10^9 (27, p. 50). In psychology, the access to the data, except those of the simplest sort, has been difficult. This may account for the neglect of such a psychological concept as belief.

2

Psychology is the study of the human circuit and its various stages, beginning with the stimulus coming from material objects and ending with the response in its effect upon material objects. Generally speaking, the order of the circuit runs from: (i) material objects; through (ii) learning; (iii) belief; (iv) memory; (v) thought; and finally to (vi) action. Let us consider each of these briefly as they concern the psychological investigator.

(i) The psychological circuit, it may be supposed, is superimposed upon the neurophysiological circuit. The latter is familiar enough: it involves the stimulus from a material object impinging upon a sensory mechanism of afferent impulses, and a central system which translates these into efferent impulses of a motor mechanism (26). Psychology has not taken into account sufficiently the relevance of the specificity of the material object which is the source of the stimulus. In fact, what saves psychology from collapsing into neurophysiology is the dependence of behavior on material objects, chiefly on those which are products of human workmanship, here called artifacts. They are of two kinds: tools made by men, and signs invented by men. These are the objective components of cultures, and are no less objective for having been fashioned by human labor from physical materials and signs. Artifacts enter into most social relations. Stimulation comes from other human individuals and effects are exerted upon them chiefly by such means. That is to say, human relations are rarely direct but are usually mediated by tools or symbols. The establishment of such interaction is accomplished by means of institutions, such as, for instance, the institution of marriage or education. Institutions usually require material objects of both kinds: tools, such as buildings—"machines for living," and charters employing the language of symbols (7).

Thus far, the study of the material objects of culture has been confined to anthropology. And so it should be. Psychology has recognized the existence of individual human behavior, and has even gone so far as to see that such behavior is not arbitrary or altogether subjective: behavior is not merely behavior as such but is always behavior about something, and "about something" usually means "about some tool or sign." And so where anthropology has studied the material object and biology the organism, psychology ought to study the interaction between them. It is true of course that natural objects will have the same effect as man-fashioned objects; but the simple fact is that individual man is a member of society and lives in the midst of some culture, and most of the stimuli that affect him, though by no means all, are artifactual. Other human individuals can stand in the same capacity, of course. But Pavlov's dogs behave in certain ways in accordance with material stimuli: food, bells, electric shock; and so do the rats of modern behaviorism: they are conditioned by mazes and other stimulus situations. It should be no great shock that the analysis of human behavior can be conducted along the same lines. The stimuli provoke the responses, but hitherto it is the responses alone which have been studied. However, if the response is a function of the stimulus and varies with it, then the character of the stimulus is a great deal more important that anyone has thought it to be, and the analysis of the tool or sign may serve as a clue to the character of the response it invokes. In other words, in any behavioral situation, we must know more about the artifact which constitutes the stimulus if we are to understand the response which constitutes the behavior.

Thus material objects are to be recognized in psychology when they serve as the sources of stimuli. At the present time they are recognized as the sources of stimuli, but not as being themselves integral elements of the psychological subject-matter. The psychological situation is not merely a response situation, as psychologists seem to suppose currently that it is; it is a *stimulus*-response situation and involves the entire situation. Psychology, then, as a science has the task of studying the material object as stimulus and the human individual as response, the effect of tools and symbols upon human individuals and not merely the isolated human individuals. The psychological subject-matter is a complex of mixed elements: material objects molded into tools by human action, and then the reaction of human individuals to those tools as responses to stimuli. In the final account of the psychological situation the material object must be included, and the type of the object must be considered in its role as stimulus and the stimulus recounted in the response that is made to it by the human individual.

Psychology properly begins with the study of sensations and perceptions, considered as responses to tools and signs in the meanings assigned. Sensation and perception were once held to be closely associated, but they are drawing apart. Sensation is lower in the scale and for the most part passive; while perception is higher and largely active. *Gestalt* concepts have noticeably altered our theories of perception, so that now perception is held to be a form-reading function, an integrative affair in which the sensory signals are "read" in a way calculated to make them conform to previously conceived diagrams. But on the other hand, the analysis of incoming signals in terms of previous experience reaches as high as cortical levels (21, p. 6) . Central and peripheral areas share the honors (although unequally) at this point in the investigation. However, what is important here is that the process is externally initiated, the senses being what they are, and this drives the problem back somewhat, for it is necessary to ascertain just when and how the conceptual diagrams are first put together.

According to Piaget, there are no absolute preconceptions, but the human individual when an infant accumulates from his experience such ideas as things in time and space. As he thus acquires an organized scheme, he assimilates to it the lessons gained from further experiences. In short from sensorimotor activity the individual moves through ego-centric representation and on into rational thought (17). This could be interpreted to mean that the character of the criteria for admission to belief increases in complexity. For thought occurs at every stage in the psychological circuit, but begins with the conditioning that the stimulus of artifacts imposes. In endeavoring to estimate what is to be accepted as true, two kinds of mental activity occur. One consists in grasping the inner structure of data (i.e., imagination or induction), while the other follows a procedure that can be described in terms of hypotheses and expectations (i.e., deduction). Adaptation of organism to environment, which is a broader way of looking at the reconciliation of artifacts, operates by means of thought.

(ii) A great step forward was taken by Pavlov (4) when he studied learning as conditioning, the implanting of habit patterns which could be reliably expected to recur. Pavlov was studying the physiology of the digestive glands; but his work has been taken up by psychologists as suggesting a fruitful line of inquiry in all studies of stimulus-and-response approaches to learning (10). Behind this phenomenon, according to British investigators (8), lies the association of ideas by contiguity, but a number of workers in the United States have endeavored to set up theories of learning based on other principles: the mechanistic theory of Guthrie according to which the proper signals invoke a contraction of muscle in some well-established order; Hull's reinforcement theory based on response to pleasure and pain; Tolman's theory of the purposive behavior of the whole organism in terms of chosen goals (25).

Most behavior in human adults is not motivated exclusively

by biological needs but could include also needs at the physical, chemical, psychological and cultural levels. The external stimulus could be initiated from any one of the integrative levels, and within the individual it reverberates among the levels; and the same two statements could be made for the internal response. Conditioning theories of learning seem confined to the biological. But it remains to be shown that motivation is simple in the human individual. Multiple motivation is more likely to be the case. A mixture of motives and of their proportions is difficult to untangle experimentally. Pavlov's method is more suitable to the study of purely biological drives as they occur in animals other than man; for man there is yet a method to be discovered adequate to the complexity of the elements involved. Drives, and reinforcement, need reduction, discrimination learning, and all of the rest of the elaborate conceptual paraphernalia invented to account for the many subtle differences that are to be found when Pavlov's method is applied to the study of human beings, are adequate for the simple reason that they merely extend and render subtle a method which remains essentially the same. Instead of advances in abstract theories, intricate experimental designs involving complex statistical computations are substituted, leading to advances in which the gain in knowledge diminishes. Learning is not followed into belief where it naturally leads. Instead it is considered as an end. But the learning process which began with the artifact is meaningful only in terms of the subsequent stage of belief, and not understandable in isolation.

(iii) The pursuit of some line of investigation should not be interpreted as inhibiting others, for as Pierce properly said (16), science should be occupied with the business of opening doors and not of closing them. The investigation of the nature of belief was abandoned too soon in psychology and ought to be reintroduced. Learning occupies the forefront of current investigations, but what is learned is remembered; and it is part of memory which is retained but not recalled with which we are concerned in the psychological concept of belief. A belief is the feeling that a proposition is true. The degree of strength of belief is susceptible to measurement. Beliefs range all the way from casually entertained thoughts to convictions of which one is ordinarily not aware but for which one is prepared to die. Weak beliefs contain a feeling of conviction quite easily dispensed with; strong beliefs consist in an emotional charge of a certain kind hooked up to a pretentious proposition. The type of belief is commensurate with the type of acceptance. Extreme beliefs are accepted only by means of extreme procedures. For instance, absolute belief is adopted under conditions of extreme emotional stress, such as the "brainwashing" conversions to communism conducted by the Chinese. There is a parallel between the shock induced in Pavlov's dogs, religious conversions and communist conversions, as William Sargant has noted (22).

When we are attempting to study a belief, we mean that we want to know three things about it: what are the reasons for holding it, how strong is the belief itself, and what actions would normally follow from it. Now there are two kinds of belief: particular beliefs, or rather beliefs about particulars (these are the recorded sense impressions which have accumulated over the years), and general beliefs, or beliefs involving universals (these are the universal propositions held to be true). Often evidence for members of the second group comes from members of the first group, but they are quite distinct nevertheless, and it is the second group which guides our actions.

How are the propositions presupposed in belief and how do actions follow from them? It is the first question which concerns us here; the second will be postponed until action is discussed. The two most important mental operations at this stage are decision and belief. Decision moves between learning and belief to propose and select propositions for consideration, and again between belief and memory to determine which propositions shall be adopted. Thought is voluntary decision-making. Conscious thought, which is studied under the heading of induction or imagination, deduction or logic, functions mentally as a species of decision-making and leads to action. Memory is merely the storehouse for belief. Decisions are the mental operations performed on candidates for belief to reject propositions as unworthy of acceptance or to store them in memory as beliefs.

(iv) The mind is a function of the body through memory; for memory makes consciousness possible, and without consciousness there could be no deliberate thought. Even memory is treated chiefly from its aspect of access: for instance, the psychologist is concerned with memory only as retention and recall, for these under present circumstances lend themselves to measurement. But what is the condition of memories as retained and before recall? These are surely equally important questions, and the possibility of obtaining some answer for them is implied by the investigation of recall mechanisms and retention span. From the curve of forgetting as found by Ebbinghaus to the more recent *Gestalt* memory traces and Freudian repressions, a number of investigators have sought theories that could be tested and means of testing them. As yet no method has been found of coming to grips with the problem of just what memory itself is. Forgetting is the failure of memory, retention is the function of memory, and recall is the use of memory.

In memory there must be something learned and retained. In order to be retained, there must be something, e.g., an image, and an attitude toward it, i.e., a belief. A memory is then a percept or a concept accompanied by a belief. The image may be the faint kind that accompanies a concept learned by means of symbols or the strong kind learned through sense perception. In all cases, it must be accepted to some extent, which is to say believed. What we believe we do not think of as beliefs but as knowledge: information gained in the past but not confined to the past in its generality. We remember a past particular fact or the particular occasion upon which a general proposition whose truth we accept was learned.

Memory no doubt exists at every level within the organism. Memories peculiar to the motor level are called habits; they are built into the muscles as learned responses. Other "memories" consist in dispositions to trigger biochemical reactions; organic "memories" must also exist as correlates of what is found at the psychological level in the passage from deliberate responses to automatic responses. Such memories, as Bergson pointed out (2), are also to be found at higher levels, habits which might be described as dispositions to think in certain ways because we have long thought in those same ways. These are not memories proper to the psychological level as much as they are memories in a position deliberately to be recalled.

(v) The manipulation of remembered material in the form of abstractions accompanied by images is termed thought. It occurs, of course, in many different forms, each of which presents a whole nest of problems (6, pp. 147–172). The solving of problems, the making of decisions, the discovery of ideas (i.e., "concept formation"), each has its own area of interest and its own technique of approach. The cognitive approach to problem-solving involves the combination and recombination of sets of variables. Thinking as such involves two distinct but intimately related sorts of activities: the choice of axioms by inductive insight, and the deductive derivation of theorems from the axioms by means of selected rules of inference. Problem-solving behavior is confronted with the complex fact represented by multiply-caused motivation and the consequent interference phenomena. Sharp differences also present themselves when a solution is required for a practical problem or for the discovery of theoretical problems, say (23). The former seems easier for team performance, while the latter is exclusively the prerogative of the originative individual. Ability to think in terms of concrete objects is far more common than the ability to think in terms of abstract objects. Decision-making has to do with probabilities; strategies based on previous experiences have to be included in the calculation, and there are of course other factors more difficult of access. Symbols to be manipulated or invented representing elements of some type in the external world: material objects or events, or abstracted relations of the same, necessitating a concentration on their abstract, image-accompanied form, come marked, so to speak, with their origin in environmental probabilities.

(vi) The long circuit from initial perceptions as the result of stimuli from artifacts, through learning, belief, memory and thought, issues in overt behavior of some sort, verbal behavior or motor activity. Thought is sometimes held to be a variety of sublingual behavior; but in any case a definite relation exists between meaning and motor activity, language employed in order to influence the action of others. In the case of skills, motor activity has been learned and then has increased through practice.

Actions are the results of beliefs, but the beliefs have to be acquired through perception, the perceptions related and stored in memory until called out by relevant situations demanding action. In order to show the position of action in the behavior of response we shall have to revert to our remarks concerning decision-making. In the same way that there was time for decision-making, so in the breathing-space between belief and action (and often this is of extremely long duration), there is room for thought. In action a further step is required, and it is supplied by the will. If one believes something strongly enough, and thought has decided what ought to be done about it, then one has character; but it is the will which takes over. Will is the ability to take action (or refrain from action) as a consequence of belief, and character is strength of will. If the will is strong enough (i.e., if there is sufficient character), action will be the result once belief has been translated into the demand for action.

Thus the messages which are taken in through the sensory organs result eventually in messages which are put out through the muscles. The psychological term for impulse is action, the "will" has been abandoned in psychology; it has gone the way of "belief": neither term is to be found currently in the psychological literature. What was covered by the "will" is now partly treated in abnormal psychology under "aggression." It is true that the "will" as an entity was highly suspect and represented some sort of oversimplification. Much more was involved than could be reified in this way. But it did cover a certain definite area and it therefore ought to be reintroduced.

Between the sensory beginnings and motor endings lie the long and highly complex processes studied by the science of psychology in its various branches and subdivisions. Action in its effect on artifacts consists in instrumental skill sequences obtained as a result of sensorimotor associations. Thus once more we are back with the proprioceptive system and with physiological variables.

Action is treated as behavior in contemporary psychology, but what is not considered is that behavior is part of a circuit which leads off from the stimulation of material objects and issues back in effects upon them. We are at the point of the object again, which is where we started; only this time with material object and action reversed; for where we began with the effect of a material object on action, we are now confronted with the effect of action on the material object, and this last stage will constitute the first stage of a new cycle. That such objects—tools and signs—are human products argues nothing against their independent effect upon human behavior, which can be as much a response to something previously made as to something adventitiously non-human in the natural world. For what we are confronted with at this end-stage is an altered material object which thus constitutes a new stimulus; whatever is done to it makes it capable of a new effect. And so there is a feedback mechanism operating between material object and organism and the establishment of a circuit.

If we are to consider psychology a science, then we shall have to assume that the domain of the psychological reaches as far up in the integrative levels as social psychology, and assume within it the artificial componentry which furnishes the stimuli for behavioral response. Psychiatry, which is the pathology of social psychology, will have to regard behavior in its aspect as response and not as an isolate valid apart from its stimulus. And the probing instruments will have to be considered also in their character as stimuli, alike whether material tool, such as tranquillizer, or symbolic object, such as the language of psychiatric interview.

It might be well now to cast the summary in the form of suggestions as to possible lines of further inquiry. In light of the foregoing argument, the progress of psychiatry as a science might take the following direction. It might: (1) disestablish the false dichotomy of "mind-and-matter" in favor of substantial forms uncovered at integrative levels. It might: (2) investigate the cultural circuit from stimulus to response. (3) It might investigate the depth and mechanism of belief and will. And finally, it might (4) include in the analysis of human behavior the character of the material object conceived as stimulus, where the response is a function of the stimulus, and not the reverse.

CHAPTER 2

THE CULTURAL CIRCUIT IN PSYCHOLOGY

NEUROPHYSIOLOGICAL AND PSYCHOLOGICAL FOUNDATIONS

THE next step is to offer a contribution to the understanding of how men behave in society. The argument rests on an hypothesis with respect to the existence of a cultural circuit in psychology and psychiatry. Psychological considerations will be treated in this chapter and psychiatric considerations in the next. Accordingly, two chief additions to the current findings in these sciences will be proposed here. These are first, the changes effected by the orientation of the human organism toward material objects, and secondly, revisions necessitated by the consideration of the integrative levels.

In every instance of the study of the behavior of animals, we have to ask ourselves some questions concerning the effect of the environment upon them. And when we do so it is necessary to remember that the animals are themselves products of the environment and engaged in a constant process of interchange with it. For the most part, it is not the entire environment that takes part in the interchange, but only that part of the environment within reach. But it is the whole animal. Thus the effect of the environment on the animal is greater than the effect of the animal on the environment. There is an effect on the environment, however, and an important one. As a matter of fact, men have made considerable alterations in their environment. It is to a large extent the result of their activities. Thus the study of human behavior can hardly leave out the material objects by which men are surrounded and which they have had a hand in the making. If the science of psychology has concentrated on the organism to the exclusion of the environment, when it was supposed to study the relationships between organism and environment, as Brunswik says (6, pp. 5–32), then it is because the environment was represented only by an object that was kept non-specific, reference being made to nothing more particular, say, then the ecological field in which broad space relationships furnish the cues. What are needed instead are specific organized material objects as cuesources.

In certain aspects of behavior theory the study of effects is undertaken in order to determine causes, and there is some danger of faulty design in committing the logical error of affirming the consequent. In addition, the statistical studies of responses are made to yield results on the method of inverse probability. However, much valuable material has been uncovered in the course of learning investigations. The difficulty lies, perhaps, in the arbitrary limits of the conception of stimulus and response as an isolable subject-matter.

Despite the introduction of cybernetic notions into neurophysiology, much remains to be done with it in psychology. The attempt will be made here, then, to construct an hypothesis to enlarge and extend the feedback mechanism into a cultural circuit which would incorporate artifacts within the model of the servomechanism. But before this can be done, some preliminary definitions are necessary.

By "psychological circuit" will be meant the cognitional level of stimulus and response extended to include a material object in a negative feedback in which the bias of the drive can be shifted, i.e., a tuneable homeostat. The negative feedback, it will be maintained, operates in this case between artifact and central nervous system in a complex set of interactions. The model of negative feedback replaces the stimulus-response model which has been the standard for some time, but the negative feedback is not an adequate model unless the material object, which is the source of the original stimulus and the recipient of the final response, is included in the circuit. For the circuit, as McCulloch pointed out, extends beyond the somatic organism (23) and is constructed to include some segment of the environment (22, p. 70). The activation of such a circuit is of course continuous. Negative feedback models when employed in psychology characteristically overlook the importance of the role played by the artifact. The consideration of the psychological subject in its aspect as servomechanism calls for the interaction with arlifacts to the consequent alteration of both subject and artifact. The continual modification of the subject by responses changes the available cues and hence the stimuli, and eventually even the responses themselves, which issue again in further modifications. Previous stimuli have the effect of conditioning the reception of later stimuli. After a sufficient number of operations, such repeated interactions construct a network of relationships between organisms and material objects in the available environment sufficient to carry the functioning of the psychological subject.

By "cultural circuit" will be meant that circuit which results from the substitution of another person (or other persons) for the artifact in the psychological circuit, with the modifications and additions consequent upon such substitution.

By "artifact" will be meant a material object altered through human agency. Thus a fence is an artifact. A tree is not, unless it has been grafted or its growth in some way influenced, but a formal garden is. The term must be conceived as possibly covering a collection of artifacts, such as a house, or an artifactual system, such as a capital city. The use of the term "artifact" here needs to be distinguished from the biological use of the term in which it denotes material faults in experimental technique, and from the archaeological use in which it is reserved for the material objects found in the unearthing of past cultures. In the sense intended throughout this chapter, the living person is profusely surrounded by artifacts of a present culture.

By "available environment" will be meant that part of the environment with which an organism effectively interacts. It interacts presumably with the total environment, but the presence or absence of food, air or other and similar organisms may affect it more specifically than Arcturus or Betelguese. The milieu, the immediate, available environment of the human individual, consists in artifacts and other persons.

There are three integrative levels with which we shall be concerned. These are: the neurophysiological, the psychological and the cultural. At the neurophysiological level, we are dealing with simple types of returnable circuits, at the psychological level with full servomechanisms, and at the cultural level with servomechanisms having tuneable homeostats. For example consider a correlative event; this would be noted in neurophysiology as a movement, in psychology as an action and in culture as behavior. The conception of laminated integrative levels in the central nervous system is not new. Toward the end of the nineteenth century Hughlings Jackson had posited the existence of levels of activity in the central nervous system (15). Ascending sensorimotor impulses traverse spinal, brain stem and thalamic projections. The tendency to find three separate but related structures within the central nervous system is in fact widespread. Galambos, for instance, finds that he can account for learning, motivation and attention by reference to the traditional afferent pathways, to the limbic midbrain circuit, and to the reticular formation, respectively (9, pp. 288–291). Consistent with this would be Bradley's hypothesis that there are three sites of action for drugs and consequently three distinct receptors in the central nervous system: the brain stem reticular formation, the diffuse thalamic projection system, and the afferent input into the reticular formation (3, pp. 123–47, esp. 146–7).

The neurophysiological circuit has been described in terms of axodendritic-synaptic transmissions along a reflex arc, and the cortical mapping of receptors has been in progress for some time; but lately it has begun to appear to be far more complicated and non-linear. We have been accustomed to thinking of stimulus and response or of conditioned and unconditioned responses, thus gradually ignoring the stimulus. But as has been pointed out, the circuit is returnable, and we need it again to account for interactions; hence we are concerned to note the effect produced by any changes within it. For instance, there is some evidence that the brain stem reticular formation exercises efferent control over afferent impulses so that the organism to some extent selects what shall influence it. To say, however, that the organism chooses those sensory stimuli by which it intends to be affected means only that the discrimination of complex stimulus patterns is conducted in terms of the previous history of such interactions. Receptors operating as far along as the brain stem function also as regulators: exciting or inhibiting (8, 12, 18, 20, pp. 177–86).

The entire mechanism of the central nervous system is geared to keep the organism in contact with the material objects of the external world. It is true, of course, that the nervous system has other functions; but then it is capable of simultaneous diverse activity (4, pp. 352–53) and there is a dynamics of the whole brain (16, pp. 151–52). We shall have to take into consideration the effect of the psychology of objects in the solid state in motion relative to the observer, with the artifact as a sequence of values of stimulus-variables and its image as a projection of the world (11, pp. 8, 51-4, 63). Psychology has been oriented altogether in the direction of the subject but studies the interaction between macrocosmic artifacts and microcosmic neurons.

The stimulation of a subject by an artifact goes through a psychological circuit to produce a response which issues in effects on the artifact; and this sequence reactivates the circuit. The effect of an artifact on a psychological subject, in other words, is stretched to include the effect of the subject on the artifact. And this effect can itself constitute a second negative feedback mechanism: the artifact, to some extent at least, operates in conformity with its own structure, often in unanticipated ways; and, as we shall see later, the inter-action is often focused on a second person. This in brief is the psychological circuit, and, when an other-person is substituted for the artifact, it is the cultural circuit. Such energy interchanges are necessary for the maintenance of steady states. The circuit begins before the stimulus, with the artifact responsible for it, and continues after the artifact receives the impact of the response in a series of self-modifying loops.

If psychology is the study of the relations between organism and environment, is, in fact, human ecology, then the stimuli can no longer be the monotonous, anonymous and undifferentiated affairs they have been thought to be but instead must be taken into the account by means of a more active and specific description. The organism lives in the environment from which it first issued, and continues to be subject to influences from that environment. Sherrington believed that the distance-receptors, and vision in particular, are necessary to the development of highly integrated reactions and even to memory (31). We must look for conceptual cues outside the subject, therefore, and independently of the reflex arc. These are to be located in a material object in space and, since they are repeated, also in time. It is only when we begin to have regard for their connection with the organism that we can consider them in their aspect as distal stimuli and as having their effects upon proximal sensory inputs. But the emphasis in this study must be placed on distal rather than proximal variables, and we must look for the meaning of the exteroceptively-evoked response.

Patterns of instinctive behavior are fired by impulses initiated somewhere between distal stimuli and the central process. The process begins with primitive probings involving sensory contact: with such efforts as visual scanning, auditory attentiveness and manipulation, each prompted by curiosity. Not enough has been said about the effect of the sensory receptors as mutual reinforcers which operate here to constitute a generalized drive: the object-oriented integration of the organism. The descending functional projection system must be conceived as extending to goal-objects. Multiple perception, the coordination of the various sense receptors on a single material object or artifact, requires that each percept in immediate perception be read as a fragment which multiple perception validates as a whole (7). Cognition and behavior are the processes which accept or correct the original perceptions.

Perception itself is a skill of the qualitative variety. The activity of selection is conditioned not only by the history of interests but also by training. However, nothing perceptual may be regarded as a simple response. The stimulus has two parts: the reception of cues from the artifact and the transmission of afferent impulses along the nerve fibers. Response itself occurs later and is far more sophisticated even at the level of the psychological circuit. The psychological circuit operates continually; so far as stimulation by the same artifact is repeated, it begins the support of inferential material; for there is the primitive discrimination between the source of the stimulus and the content of the stimulus; in short, a message. According to recent researches, it is the posterior intrinsic system, the reticular brain stem, which functions in the gathering of information (1, 26, 29).

In general it may be asserted that the drives are based on the objective and external integrative levels in which the goals exist: survival on the physical level, hunger on the biological, sex on the psychological and curiosity on the cultural. In every instance, of course, the goal-seeking occurs in terms of specific natural objects: the pursuit of a state of health, the search for food, a mate or the knowledge of an explanation. Motivation is in evidence equally on the negative side: the avoidance of an enemy or threat, and of stimulation by pain, hunger pangs, sexual craving, and doubt, respectively. Many other drives do exist, as illustrated by Tolman's list (35, p. 220), but these are the fundamental ones. Genetically of course each of the levels is chronologically later as well as structurally higher. There are no precise boundaries; each level presupposes the ones below it and rises qualitatively above.

We are interested in the cultural level, and of course its dependence upon the reflex arc is assumed. It is not to the purpose here to elaborate the functioning of the receptors, conduction along the afferent nerve fibers, or central impressions involving spinal cord or brain stem, although the thalamic integration of sensory impulses is suggestive. And later we shall not be concerned to follow the steps whereby contact is made with motor cells and conduction resumed along efferent pathways to the terminals in the tissues of muscle fibers, even though the fact that skilled movements are probably initiated in connection with the precentral gyrus is relevant. This is the neurophysiological circuit, and it is more primitive and more fundamental than the psychological circuit. At this point it should be remembered that the lower integrative levels determine higher: causes always lie at one integrative level lower than effects, simpler causes producing complex effects. The structure apposite to the present purpose is higher and is superimposed upon the lower neurological processes by which it is carried. Equilibrium is a steady state; and a steady state at a given level, say the psychological, requires a fixed rate of change at the next lower level, say the neurophysiological. The behavior of an organism could be predicted by the probabilities of an open system given sufficient information about the initial structure as a complex set of variables.

In a certain sense, the organism is helpless in the hands of the data. The world is larger than man and he must accommodate himself to it, not it to him. Reliance on the world is continuous and contact with it is never broken. Consciousness seems to be made possible by the balanced functioning of the reticulo-hypothalamic-cortical system (10, pp. 222–23), but the fact that uniform stimulation produces loss of consciousness indicates a neurological dependence on the external world (36, p. 378). Long ago, Hobbes observed that "it is all one to be always sensible of the same thing and not to be sensible of anything" (14), and Mill knew that "all consciousness is of difference" (27). We are not aware of our receptors but of objects beyond them, and it is those objects which play a necessary cortical role (10, pp. 191, 425). Consciousness, then, is consciousness *of* something, and that something has to be discriminated which it could not be were there no differences.

Every artifact from the point of view of the organism's awareness of it consists in an infinite set of cues, visual, tactile, auditory, etc., contained as information display variables. Large areas of the cerebral cortex are evidently required to function simultaneously in order to provide for the adjustment of the organism to the environment. It is part of the inherently extended nature of sensory experience that every contact with an artifact makes more of an impression on the organism than is needed for the interaction. The result is a dynamic effect on the organism's selection of its subsequent cues and the initiation of a recursive circuit.

The analogy with engineering psychology holds. The artificer may be considered a monitor of programmed operations, and his responses as measuring the recognition of the state of the system. Such responses issue in the stimulation of artifacts, by revised programming. True, the organism exercises a certain measure of control over what will constitute stimulation. In particular, it would seem that the frontal and limbic systems are responsible for the adjustment of perturbations in dispositional states. But once a stimulus (i.e., an artifact or an artifactual situation) has been elected for the focusing of attention, the force of the arousal is determined by the extent to which the stimulus departs from expectation or contains an element of surprise.

Curiosity is a basic tissue need of the neuronal aggregates. It orients responses in proportion as the stimulus introduces surprises. To understand what modifications are made in the afferent activity, it would be necessary to know what modifications had already been made in the central nervous system by such activity previously; we have argued already that there are modifications in what may be characterized as a subsidiary feedback. Monkeys do exhibit curiosity; but the gratification of inquiry in man requires the inclusion of artifacts and inter-personal relations extending into the external world far beyond any sensation of pleasure that can be reached by stimulation through chronically implanted electrodes. There exists a complexity of interactions, so that to formalize the discharge of receptors, to ground neurally the rudimentary intuitions representing impressions, in short to comprehend fully the operation which takes place between artifactual cues and subjective reception, involves the knowledge of a code to which we do not yet have the key.

From the neurophysiological model of the organism as a simple mechanism in which responses are wholly controlled by the stimuli, to the more complex conception of an organism which can to a large extent influence the character of its stimulation, either by selection or alteration of the artifact, is not a change in theory but merely a building to higher levels. The all-or-nothing reaction of the reflex arc remains; what is superimposed upon it is the graded response of the neuronal aggregates. The sophisticated stimulus is the action exercised *upon* artifacts; the sophisticated response is the action exercised *by* artifacts; and these are not the same. To understand the role of the organism in an environment, it is necessary to consider the stimulus constituted by its role as artificer, to trace a response constituted by its role as operator, and to understand the code by which they are connected.

Appetitive-consummatory processes in the case of the basic tissue need of curiosity will nominally consist in the thirst for, and the acquisition of, knowledge. The organism wants to know how it should act under certain circumstances even though the occasion never arise, and this knowledge is to be found in the effects of its previous actions. Thus it is that impulses in the circuit travel a parabolic route between artifactual and subjective poles. Knowledge is for the sake of action, but also learning requires the alteration of artifacts; experiments in the physical sciences, for example, conducted for purposes of inquiry. Thus the acquisition of knowledge involves a circuit which begins and ends with the artifact.

Impression leads to retention by validating the correspondence between artifact and cognition. Retention involves a change of state in the neurons; in some way we do not as yet understand, the excitation of tissue is involved in the recording and storing of information so that the engram is made responsible for the proper recall. The storing of information involves its rearrangement as complex systems of strategies; in the lower animals patterns of instinctive behavior, in man the preparation of abstract structures for use as tactics. Memory, in a word, anticipates behavior.

Retained material is not, however, quiescent; there is an internal background of neural activity. Berger's alpha rhythm is abolished by conscious mental activity, but not so the higher frequency beta waves; and the delta waves are still present in sleep. No matter how far the environmental stimuli are reduced (they cannot be eliminated altogether from a living organism), there would appear to be some activity, often even seemingly self-generated and prolonged, perhaps organizational in character (28, p. 337). For there is information already present and in need of working over. Also, there is continuous input whether or not there is recall, and such modifications take the form of stimuli which intrude upon the internal background without disturbing the foreground of focused attention. As further messages are received, they are sorted; some are relevant, others not. The relevant messages function to modify the retained material.

At the neurophysiological level tissue needs prepare responses for triggering by appropriate external stimuli. At the psychological level also, releasing mechanisms operate in connection with innate behavior patterns. Retained beyond these, however much they may affect certain dispositions, are others of a more established character. Sunk deep into the tissue of the neuronal aggregates are the stable dispositional states. The circuit from artifactual stimulus to responses issuing in action upon artifacts would appear to have been interrupted, but it has been merely postponed. A belief is a delayed response. Should the occasion never arise to trigger it into action, the delay may be permanent, but the belief remains, retained in the tissues in which it can in fact become incorporated.

Stability of behavior involves the retention of a disposition to act. But there were already other dispositions. The patient has collected a history, and the more cumulative the more determinative. From the innumerable and continuous transactions between stimulus and subject, there has emerged slowly the construction of a private retention schema.

By "private retention schema" here is meant an unconscious set of experientially acquired and emotionally accepted and endorsed dispositional states. The private schema has a core of stability but a peripheral area of change. It requires and receives occasional reinforcement. We shall see in the next section that there is also a public schema, and the elements of the two schemata are rarely sorted. Since there is evidence that the brain stem reticular formation functions in the waking states (24, pp. 1–20; 25), it is probable that the retention schemata are cortically related.

Representation occurs only while a proposition is being transacted. The proposition is then represented by its corresponding feeling. Abstraction may result from the closing of the neural network and the consequent reverberation of the message. Dispositions to act are reinforced through the repetition of behavior patterns until habit furnishes recognizable degrees of associative strengths. Intentions tend not only to persist but also to concentrate; habit rolls them up into something solid and almost substantial. But actions are necessary to maintain dispositional states, if the continual contact with artifacts is to constitute a recursive circuit.

A dispositional state is knowledge looked at from the nature of its apprehension. If a disposition is a delayed response, there is always the possibility of a response. The spontaneous discharge of receptors can be interpreted as one variety of delayed response. The continuous excitation of the psychological circuit involves the extended activity of the cortical cells. Centrally aroused sensations can occur after such extended activity. In many cases of the excitation of neuronal aggregates, the response exceeds in duration and frequency the initial stimulation. This, too, can have its pathological exaggeration. Impressions made are tissue memories; they can be recalled. The recall of unconscious beliefs is a result of organic-level behavior patterns. Instinctive actions represent unconscious beliefs. Taxis-controlled motions point to dependence on the original stimuli of the artifact now functioning as the recipient of the effects of innate motor patterns. There can be at this level completeness of motor patterns discharged without biological meaning, such as the displacement behavior studied by Lorenz, Tinbergen and others, in which a frustrated instinctive action is discharged into the channels of another and quite different instinctive action (21, 30, p. 298; 33; 34).

We shall see that in the case of conscious beliefs, the recall is stimulated deliberately (the will). A conditioned response under the direction of self-controlled receptors when engaged in the act of anticipation becomes a servomechanism. Voluntaristic impulses travel a negative feedback circuit. The subject remembers what it is that he believes, only this time in terms of the action singled out, of what it was that he wanted to do. There are motor patterns to be called upon there. Drive-reduction is brought about by the exercise of motor skills, but first there must be an incentive and an expectancy. For the most part, goal-setting is focused on the alteration of artifacts. The motivations are not furnished by other human individuals as they are at still higher levels, but the humans get dragged along in the wake of such alterations. The pathological aspect in this connection is the anxiety involved in the anticipation of failure. The aspiration toward achievement-levels is dependent upon a cognitional approach, since expectancy-value is measured by awareness of skills and effects ("know-how").

There is thus one new element which occurs in the process at this point. In the psychological circuit, the subject exercises a certain measure of control over its own activities, however they may have been stimulated. The resulting changes in the artifact may or may not correspond exactly to the incentive of dispositional states, but there is an effort at control which is to some extent successful even though it may fall somewhat short. Whether or not the concept of graded response will be adopted to replace the all-or-nothing response in order to account for the control of action in higher organisms, remains to be decided by further evidence. In either case, it is clear that the role played by the cognitive consciousness has been grievously neglected. Voluntaristic alternatives are presented by the condition of the artifact; they are selected by ratiocinative methods.

The impulse to action is an imbalance and an irritation, a painful dispositional state. Equilibrium can be restored only by the appropriate action. Thus decisions are relief mechanisms designed to facilitate the evacuation of surplus emotional content. Regulatory mechanisms responsible for the maintenance of homeostasis may be partly responsible also for the discharge of impulses to action. Brain stem ventricles have been suspected of functioning as homeostats in this connection. Activity would have to be included in their zone of reference as much as other sensitivities, such as body temperature or food intake. There is, in short, a need to act, and the circuit that was initiated by artifactual cues and that now issues in muscular exertion against material resistance is one kind of appetitive-consummatory process. The functional localization made possible by efferent pathways and effector mechanisms: muscles, glands, etc., only serves to furnish clear channels. The action itself issues in the alteration of the artifact.

Thus we are back at the artifact which was the source of the original stimulus; only this time instead of furnishing cues it is the recipient of the effects, in short of action. It is in this way that the artifact is made and operated. The action transforms the artifact, which is thus in a condition to offer a fresh set of cues and ready to stimulate another set of responses and so to initiate another activation of the circuit. Gradually, as a result of repetitions of these activations, an artifactual environment is built up in such a way that the organism can determine its own stimulations. To account for this phenomenon fully, however, another element will have to be introduced.

This final element is the independent behavior of the artifact itself. In considering interactions between organism and environment, we have been assuming that the behavior of the artifact is just what the organism determines it to be. But there are after all also artifactual receptors, exemplified by such purely physical phenomena as surface resistance to contact, compression waves, deformation, etc., evidence that each artifact possesses its own organization. Small causes may give rise to large effects, and no one who initiates a course of action can successfully predict all of its consequences. The artifact to some extent leads a life of its own, exhibiting a pattern of behavior at least partly dictated by its own configurations; and this behavior often redounds to the detriment of the organism in ways which were not anticipated. Men killed by motor cars they have manufactured as the result of traffic accidents they had not intended; occupational diseases of many sorts; professional attitudes and lives—the list is a long one. The effect of the organism on the artifact is limited by the intractability of the material selected and the pattern followed; the effect of the artifact on the organism is limited by the self-contained nature of the organization of the artifact.

THE CULTURAL CIRCUIT

We have been endeavoring to separate out the various strands of the neurophysiological and psychological circuits; the former a repeating type of stimulus-response mechanism, the latter widened to include stimuli from and responses to specific material artifacts. We are now ready to extend the model further to include also inter-personal relations in the cultural circuit. This is accomplished by making alterations in the reverberating circuit in two ways: by adding in the superimposed material and by introducing the new element of the social. We shall run through the same divisions of the cultural circuit, only this time at a level of integration compelled by the new factors.

The difference between the neurophysiological and psychological circuits, on the one hand, and the cultural circuit on the other, is that in the former the tissue needs power the drives and tissue satisfactions constitute the responses and the stimulus-response mechanism and simple servomechanism are explanatory; whereas in the cultural circuit there is aim at two sorts of accomplishments: knowledge and construction. Every stimulus retains the character of a projection, and neurophysiology hooks up directly with social psychology. Superimposed higher circuits indicate connections of a transitive nature between the neurophysiological and the cultural. Culture results from the efforts of man to make the kind of world to which he would wish to accommodate himself. The adjustments of external stimuli necessary to produce the desirable responses by the organism now must be furnished by the qualities emerging from the social context. In the cultural circuit material objects and other persons are included, and the servomechanism with tuneable homeostats is the model necessary for explanation. The knowledge is knowledge about something beyond the subject, and the construction consists in artifacts, or inter-personal relations, or, as in the case of social institutions, both.

Let us assume that we are dealing with a human individual among other human individuals as well as among artifacts. Psychological patterns already exist, but strong reinforcement for some of them comes from other individuals. For this purpose, a second individual may play a dual role which he performs separately: he may be a corroborative or a combative source, or he may serve as himself an artifact. In either case, the stimulation is reinforced or weakened. The available environment for the human individual contains only other human individuals and artifacts, and they are shuffled up together in a social milieu which to be social must contain at least one of each type of element.

The corroborative stimulation from other individuals leads to belief; the combative stimulation leads (where it does not issue in overt action) to doubt. But in order to receive the impressions from other individuals which are so necessary to belief or doubt and to action, a language is required.

Languages are artifacts of a particular sort. They consist in artifacts which in the available environment indicate other artifacts and in the total environment other material objects: symbolic artifacts. A symbol is an artifactual sign, and always has a material component. A sentence in a language is a string of marks, and a string of marks can represent anything from an algebraic equation to a declaration of war. The point is that the inter-personal relations are the ones which compel the introduction of symbolic artifacts. Languages are signalling systems in use in inter-personal relations. Just as the reflex arc carries the cultural circuit, so strings of marks carry the communication of meaning. Linguistic communication functions as arousal, but arousal of a different character from what we have studied previously. It does not figure directly in the discharge of motor patterns affecting the initiating artifact but instead makes contact with more complex structures.

The reaction to external stimulation could not occur altogether on the basis of the changing elements of the external world. Some permanent elements had to be found so that there could be a stability in guidance patterns for behavior. There was needed, in short, some basis for belief, and the changing particulars of the external world proved incapable of supporting any sort of permanence of the individual material objects themselves. The stability did not develop among the particulars disclosed to sensation but rather in the configurations disclosed to cognition. Hence recurrence was detected and the symbols to represent it invented. The world of imagination was the result. What we found earlier to be true of sensory experience itself, is true also of all symbolic expression. It is part of the inherently extended nature of language that no particular can be adequately represented except in general terms. There has to be an area for the consideration of configurations. That is the domain of cognition, of thoughts-about-particulars, which is one stage in complexity beyond awareness. Thoughts-about-particulars is awareness of awareness, but it is not yet at the level of thoughts-about-generalizations, of which more shortly.

Thoughts-about-particulars consist in internal speech commenting on the observation of strong perceptual fields. Thought is not all belief; it includes the entertainment of ideas, and the consideration of the acceptance of knowledge, and such entertainment requires doubt in addition to belief. No doubt, then no reason; no reason, then no acceptance. Belief is not voluntary but always and only for reasons—what, to the believer at least, appear to be good reasons. The type of belief is commensurate with the type of acceptance. Extreme beliefs are accepted only by means of extreme procedures. A philosophy requires a revelation.

Thoughts-about-generalizations are comments on the observations of ideational graphs. The non-specific categories which have ridden in on the first generalizations govern the conclusions concerning all subsequent ones. For instance, "poltergeist" brings with it the information that there are such things as noisy household ghosts constituting a class. "Poltergeist" itself is labelled subclass, ready to be considered on the same basis as, say, "leprechaun" and these together perhaps under "spirits."

Belief is the feeling that a proposition is true when it is conscious belief, but there is also the feeling of doubt based on conflicting material. This conflict has to be resolved in the foreground and the issue returned to the background. Doubt is self-liquidating and has a shorter life. Ordinarily, one does not believe a proposition to be true but merely believes a proposition. Belief is constructed on information emotionally charged. This is because one does not hold propositions as such but accepts the reality of that to which they refer, feeling through them, as it were, to the situations to which they point. To believe that all men are mortal does not mean to believe that "all men are mortal" is true; it means to believe that each and every man, those one actually knows as well as those one does not know, will eventually die.

The inception of belief can be due to two causes other than reason: feeling and action.

We have discussed the inception of belief under the dominance of reason. There is belief also when feeling is dominant over reason. Such an occasion would have to be one starting from a strong emotional stress or tension, similar to that which Pavlov produced in his dogs. Mass conversion, whether to a religion or to a philosophy, is usually obtained by means of two mechanisms: mass suggestibility and emotional tension. Conversions to Christianity and to communism have occurred in much the same way; for instance in the former case by Spaniards who offered the Indians of the

Americas a choice of the cross or death, and in the latter case by the Chinese brainwashing of their prisoners.

The inception of belief under the dominance of action is what has long been called "learning by experience." A particular action successfully completed demonstrates the falsity of the proposition that there exists no such class of actions. Action often dramatically illustrates what cannot be done because of obstacles, and by inference what can. A burned child shuns the fire, but also a man who has synthesized a protein in the laboratory has demonstrated that proteins can be synthesized.

Many other sources of belief exist. Beliefs have been accepted because of thoughts, feelings or actions, but also on each of the following more specific grounds: analogy, authority, common sense, dreams, ego, emotion, other beliefs, forced conviction, habit, intuition, pathology, revelation, social pressure, tradition. It will be necessary for present purposes to say an additional word about two of these: other beliefs and social pressure.

Beliefs are often accepted because they are consistent with other beliefs already held. Awareness compels a need for consistency. There is pain in conflicting beliefs of which the patient is aware, and at least the discomfort of knowing that for him they are not prepared to issue in action. Beliefs consist in behavior patterns awaiting discharge, to be triggered chiefly by relevant external events. They are reinforced meanwhile by other beliefs with which they are consistent. The stronger the reinforcement the more comfortable the storage. The internal environment, the *milieu interieur,* is disturbed by conflicting beliefs and supported by consistent ones. If a problem is entertained and several solutions present themselves, it will often be the case that the one adopted offers not the best outcome but the greatest satisfaction.

There is another form of consistency among beliefs. This is the effect on the strength of a belief in one person of the fact that the same belief is accepted by many persons. It is difficult to deny and easy to believe what others believe also. Moreover, beliefs held in common by the members of a given society are beliefs in harmonic phase; they reinforce each other through resonance. Thus it is that the human organism is not a valid isolate but relies upon cultural components, chiefly symbolic communication. The resonance of beliefs is supported by inter-personal communications involving artifactual signs: writing or speech, strings of marks or of sound-waves. In the psychological circuit there are organic needs; in the cultural circuit, the needs are replaced by composition.

When beliefs multiply, simple consistency is no longer sufficient, and a complex structure of beliefs is required in order to maintain order among them. The beliefs have somehow to be organized into a system, in which, of course, consistency remains the criterion. This system is the public retention schema.

By "public retention schema" here is meant a system of social beliefs interpreted as rules of procedure whereby cognition is enabled on the one hand to apply its fundamental categories to sort out the data subsequently disclosed to sense experience and on the other hand to guide behavior. The primitive elements of such a system are the categories, non-specific elements of coding systems, in the sense of Bruner (5, pp. 41–67), which act as selective filters to determine how experience shall be interpreted. The experiences themselves *are* specific.

The conception of a public schema invites comparison with that of the private schema. The private schema is peculiar to a given individual; the public schema is common to all members of a given culture. The two schemata together constitute the beliefs of the individual. But there is no dead storage, as in a computer; some of the beliefs must be revised from time to time as new information is received or new relations between the bits of stored information detected. Hence the necessity for movement within the schemata.

Kant was the first to use the term, schema (17), but as employed here it is closer to the meaning given it by Head (13, pp. 605–6) and Bartlett (2, pp. 199–204, 299); it is however distinguished from these, also, by the emotional charge on its separate elements, by the degree of generalization of its contents, and by the tightly systematic nature of its organization. Bartlett finds the origin of consciousness in the ability of the human organism to recognize its own schemata, a view which goes somewhat further than the present usage. Consciousness in the theory of the cultural circuit would be merely the doubling up of awareness, as for instance in the recognition of perception.

With the public retention schema is initiated the formalization of the process of axiom-acquisition. This is accomplished in one of two ways: either by recognizing in events the compulsion to beliefs of a critical sort, beliefs capable of serving as axioms in a system; or by recognizing among the beliefs already held those which are more important and so capable of serving as axioms for the deduction of the others. To incorporate a belief into a system of beliefs is another form of reinforcement. Beliefs gain strength from the support of other beliefs and doubt is thereby rendered less probable. It is difficult to single out one element of a complex for possible rejection without involving other elements; the elements are stronger for being parts of a whole. Every belief radiates outward to logically proximate similar propositions. There is a disposition to believe in the truth of all propositions of the same class.

We shall see that the effect of the relation of beliefs is widespread and intense. First of all, however, it is necessary to consider the degrees of tenacity of belief. These range all the way from the most casual observations which pass through consciousness lightly without being remembered afterwards, such as passing thoughts, to those ultra-stable dispositional states which are held unconsciously in the memory but are capable of instigating visceral reactions at any time, such as metaphysical beliefs.

Beliefs tend to persist. A few degrees of strength of belief may be listed in the order of increasing intensity: a belief of which the subject is not at all sure; one into which he is prepared to inquire further; one on which he is prepared to bet money; one for which he is willing to take greater chances; one on which he could be asked to risk his life; one for which he is ready to die; one which he is incapable of denying; one of which he is unaware; one of which he cannot be made aware. Among beliefs, persistence may be counted as a function of intensity: the greater the intensity the longer the persistence.

Upon acceptance, beliefs begin to organize themselves into systems. With retention, two further developments occur which are of a far-ranging nature. The first of these is that thought appears.

There is some tentative evidence that for the neurophysiologist thought has its origins in the generalizing from experience engineered by the amygdaloid mechanism (32). At the psychological level, thought may be regarded as an over-determined response to the stimulus of symbol-acquisition and as consisting in the association and dissociation of ideas. Enough work has been done on deductive and inductive logic to render further discussion in the present connection nugatory. We are concerned here with deeper levels of retention. Mental events cannot be explained by means of deliberate and conscious processes alone. What we need to know is the mechanism of interaction, and this can be explained partly on the level of the association of ideas. Only, as a result of having been worked over by belief, the ideas are no longer simple logical propositions: they are now supercharged with qualities of feeling. How ideas affect one another qualitatively and not how the subject feels about them is what is meant by mental events. For it happens that only in the mind does the opportunity arise for the concrete interplay of abstractions. But since retention in the mind relies to some extent upon reinforcement from other minds, there must be some communication involved. Also, memory is limited and faulty; some other means must be found for recording material.

The two functions, communicating and remembering, come together in artifactual symbolic form. The shift of memory involving complex sequences of action from brain to symbolic artifact (e.g., sign systems in books, records, etc.) is a complex variety of human displacement behavior which has been incorporated in habit for its pragmatic value. The structure of an entity is that which is common to every segment of its history, and such structures can be arrested historically and retained by being removed from living tissues and stored in sign relationships.

The extension of thought into further stages of complexity and its attendant intensity is made possible by the interplay of attention and symbolic artifacts. There is certainly such a thing as precognitive mentality, and thoughts do occur before there is language. Levy-Bruhl argued that there is a precognitive mentality among primitive peoples (19). A notable example is the thoughts of very young children before the acquisition of speech, say under two years of age. Such thoughts, however, are rudimentary and simple. Children at such an age are incapable of putting many things together. But higher mentation takes place by means of language. Thought is self-reflective speech, and interior debate.

Thought is extended in another direction also. Just as there is a precognitive mentality, so there is a subconscious mentality. Thought of this variety is part of the continuous background of below-threshold nervous activity. Alternatives are compared and contrasted, and decisions made without the immediate awareness that such processes are in effect; but the entire mechanism of depth psychology depends upon them.

The final outcome of thought of whatever variety is a network of beliefs, the retention schemata. These are stored in the memory where they are available to releasing mechanisms. The function of releasing mechanisms is to connect up events with relevant beliefs. We have noted already that beliefs are propositions on which the feelings bestow a disposition to act. A set of beliefs, then, is a learned behavior pattern which by means of interaction with material objects or by means of inter-personal relations has been added to the already existing set of innate behavior patterns. The weakest beliefs are capable of firing only vague inclinations to action, and consist in convictions quite easily dispensed with, while the strongest have a compulsive character and carry an emotional charge.

Not all beliefs, of course, lead directly to action. All are prepared to do so but not all are called on by relevant events. Beliefs about individuals lead inductively to beliefs about generals, and beliefs about generals carry with them by deduction the anticipatory belief about uncountable individuals.

It often happens that the making of a connection between belief and action is unconscious, mere taxis-controlled behavior. At higher integrative levels it is of course conscious, and is called the will, a kind of rule of inference for cognition, operating between theorematic beliefs and the role of overt behavior in the field of action. The will makes possible the discharge of belief into action, an intentional response. The releasing mechanism at this level takes the form of deliberate decision. It may be triggered by beliefs when they rise to a certain level of strength, but the consequent impulse can be inhibited. A negative decision may be as effective as a positive; confronted with a relevant call, the decision not to act requires a great voluntaristic exertion. Other considerations come into play which are perhaps effective but nevertheless weaker. Character is the property of control exercised in acting (or not acting) upon a decision.

We revert at this point to the mechanism with which the analysis of the cultural circuit began, the negative feedback and the centrality of the artifact or other-person. Artifacts and other-persons are organized together in institutions. Each organism has a bias in favor of some external goal, that is the primal postulate of the theory of the cultural circuit being propounded here. The homeostatic mechanism is designed to maintain equilibrium, and the drives are to supply the balance with the necessary components. However, as goal-seeking increases, the homeostat has to be tuned to it and the balance readjusted by means of it. Thus the internal equilibrium becomes more tenuous and has to be predicated on the drive toward some external goal. To shift the goal calls for retuning the homeostat. A tuneable homeostat means in the cultural circuit the ability to change the canon of selection whereby the self is to control how it will be altered by its own alterations. The internal organism, in other words, depends upon the continuing constructive efforts of man, the maker.

The nervous system conditions behavior of a sort responsible for the construction of artifacts. Inter-personal behavior is responsible for the construction of symbolic artifacts. In both cases, the artifacts play the leading role in the modification of behavior. Artifacts constitute the instruments which organisms have found to modify themselves according to their own design. At the highest known integrative levels, the circuit is still active and can be observed. The mechanism of the negative feedback, operating on prepotent material, produces displacement behavior at the higher levels. For just as lower integrative levels determine higher, so higher integrative levels direct lower. An extreme example is the emotions invoked by works of art: Bach's fugues, Shakespeare's plays, Phidias' sculpture. This is what Freud recognized intuitively when he argued that the frustration of the sex drive is responsible for civilization. The displaced sex drive discharges into the production of original artifacts—tools and institutions, for example. It is precisely because he covets his neighbor's wife in vain that he builds office skyscrapers. Displacement behavior leads, in short, to releasing mechanisms capable of operating to increase control.

CHAPTER 3

TRANSFER MATCHING: A NEW METHOD IN PSYCHOTHERAPY

W E HAVE now reached the point in the argument at which a new method in psychotherapy can be proposed, one uniting the techniques currently employed separately: techniques for the indoctrination of absolute beliefs, and for the administration of electroshock. First, however, it will be necessary to present something of the background of psychopathology against which such therapy can be meaningful.

PSYCHOPATHOLOGY OF THE CULTURAL CIRCUIT

We begin with the pathology of the cultural circuit. As usual it is necessary to build on the neurophysiological and psychological circuits. It will be recalled that an equilibrium exists between organism and external goal, based on the drives: hunger at the physiological level, sex at the psychological level, and curiosity at the cultural level. Since we have been chiefly concerned with the cultural level, we confine ourselves in this connection to curiosity; the drive toward inquiry is satisfied only with manipulation: constructing an artifact or reconstructing society by participation. If the equilibrium is upset, a disturbance ensues. It can be upset by mechanisms at any of the three levels.

We have seen that genetically the psychological level is higher than the neurophysiological and also later in the evolutionary series, and the cultural level is still higher and even later. The historical development is the basis for the establishment of a norm.

We begin where we left off in the study of the cultural circuit. Remembering, then, that lower integrative levels are causal for the higher levels and the higher levels directive for the lower, it should not be surprising that brain damage impairs intelligence. The plausible hypothesis has been offered that with damage to the limbic system the biased homeostats of the internal core brain stem are freed so that errors are not corrected and oscillation results, as suggested by Pribram and others (3, pp. 8–15). A good example of such oscillation is to be seen in the behavior of the typical schizophrenic, who when confronted with emotional stimuli either retreats into a state of apathy or over-reacts, the generalized inhibition of movement and the extreme muscular aggression of the catatonic, for instance.

Pribram's hypothesis can be extended in several directions. If errors are not corrected, then signals from the external world can be ignored. As in studies of ablation, deficiencies as well as releasing mechanisms make their appearance. The organism is turned inward and a pathological subjectivity results. There is some reason why psychology has tended to study the organismic end of the interaction between organism and environment: there is some skewness in the normal circuit, with the concentration bunched at the organismal end. In a pathological circuit the skewness has increased. Where equilibriums had been established to facilitate the drives, equilibrium itself now becomes stronger than the drive. In fact, the drive itself is toward the restoration of equilibrium. The result is an organism inadequately in contact with the available environment. As a result the subjectivity increases, and signals are looked for only from within the organism.

When homeostasis no longer relies upon exteroceptive stimuli, there must be other neurological symptoms. It would be interesting to know, for instance, whether in the psychotics any subtle shifts occur in sensitivity or foreground functioning from the parasympathetic to the sympathetic nervous systems, from exteroceptors to proprioceptors. Certainly such a shift would explain why all illnesses, from fractured tibia to poliomyelitis, are accompanied by psychic trauma.

Genetically speaking, the process of development from infant to adult involves the addition to the neurophysiological circuit of the psychological circuit and finally of the cultural circuit, the normal circuit of the adult. Pathology reverses genetics; it attempts to turn back the psychological clock. The pathological individual is one in whom there has been a reversion from the cultural circuit to the psychological and perhaps even in some cases to the neurophysiological. Displacement behavior makes its appearance. Motor patterns are discharged without the proper psychological goals. Orientation toward objects becomes secondary to manifest behavior, the action having taken temporal precedence, with the purpose casually fitted to it afterwards. Cues come more insistently from lower levels, but they are conflicting and confusing, and so there is an additional delay in responding to them. It is not a new story that impairment of function may be due to delayed response, and that the additional impairment may result in further disorganization.

Pathology in a word is subjectivity. When an individual encounters a conflict between his retention schemata and events, he refuses to give up the schemata and hence withdraws from the world of events. Issues between acting and knowing are settled in favor of knowing, but this can be accomplished only by shifting from the world in which action occurs to the one in which knowing occurs. The occasional procedure of introspection becomes the customary behavior. Learning from experience means revising the schemata in terms of new information; but now the schemata are no longer to be revised. The neurophysiological and the psychological organism continues, however, to live in a world of events. Stresses are produced upon the individual and strains result, the "catastrophic response" (2), with its inevitable pathological consequences.

There follows a breakdown in the structure of goal-seeking. Thus where becoming a normal adult had meant using the self to produce effects on the world, becoming a pathological adult now means using the self to produce effects upon the self which are detrimental; the result is the same kind of subjectivity which was originally the normal mental state of the child. This accounts for the resemblance in the Freudian explanation between the psychotic and the infantile. The external world with its material objects and inter-personal relations is shut out because the adjustments within the organism do not permit it to be faced in that direction. Instead, there is a concentration within the self. The greatest intensity of activity is taking place there, but at lower levels. Excitation at a lower level may inhibit functioning at a higher. Centrally aroused sensations become hyperactive in inhibiting the reception of stimuli. When the whole effort of which an organism is capable is devoted to homeostasis, the effects of all further stimuli take on a nociceptive character.

There is another equally strong result of the freeing of biased homeostats. Oscillation occasions conflict. The contradictions contained in the conflicts of stored beliefs are released by the subjective concentration, and what Festinger has called "cognitive dissonance" results (1). This is the pathology of the ratiocinative stage, but it can be subconscious. Competing beliefs can lead to interference with action, inhibitory efferent impulses cancelling afferent.

A deep feeling of insecurity compels an effort at resolution, and there is no left-over attention to turn outward. Hence the subject in this state is indifferent to events around him and he cannot be moved. The dependence shifts to the conflict, which then becomes necessary; and the conflict-dependent reaches an adjustment as a kind of equilibrium neurotic: stabilized on a balance involving high tension.

In addition to paralyzing action, cognitive dissonance can have other effects. It can for instance reinforce beliefs in irrational ways. Beliefs formerly held on evidence are now held for their stability effects. The inherently extended nature of experience leaves a residue of generality which has to be resolved. It cannot be supported as free-floating by the pathological personality, for it, too, challenges stability. Where stability maintained was a natural condition hardly regarded by the individual as it occurs in a supportable state furnished by the equilibrium between his drives and his goals, stability lost becomes a state very much the object of awareness and of desire. Consequently, the nearest equipment is seized upon and a synthetic equilibrium attempted. Prejudices are ready to hand where beliefs are unavailable. A prejudice is a belief held despite its conflict with another belief for which there is stronger evidence. With the equilibrium based on the balance between drive and external object interrupted, the attainment (or restoration) of equilibrium itself has become the drive. In the neurotic, equilibrium is restored by freezing beliefs in conflict, one or more of which may be prejudices in the sense defined above.

Let us return to the genetic pattern again. In the developing individual, both private and public retention schemata are constructed. We have seen that the private retention schema consists in those beliefs which result from specific and unique individual experience and that the public retention schema consists in those more organized beliefs which all the individuals in a given culture hold in common. Both are likely to be maintained in their essentials in the subconscious, stored in the memory. In a normal individual, the public retention schema takes precedence over the private; in a pathological individual the private retention schema struggles for precedence. But when the activity of the individual becomes subjective, the emotionally over-determined efforts to replace the lost equilibrium would appeal to just those elements in experience in which emotion had prevailed over reason. Public retention schemata are rationally founded; it would almost be possible to say that they are the same as the axioms of reason for individuals sharing a common culture. Private retention schemata vary from individual to individual and are emotionally founded.

The effort at ascendency of the private schema over the public schema has other serious effects. Among these are compulsive behavior and emotional acceptance of the public schema.

There is nothing wrong *per se* with what is called obsessive or compulsive behavior. The fear of conscience in what Freud called the compulsive type of individual is only the substitution of a subjective element (conscience) for an objective element (the love object). Compulsive behavior is not regarded as over-determined when the goal is a socially-approved and accepted element of the public schema. What is wrong—when it is wrong—is the type of element, which has become a subjective one. We have named two such elements: an equilibrium of prejudices, and the conscience. Compulsive behavior, in short, is only pathological when it is based on a drive toward some pathological object, such as the two just enumerated.

The emotional acceptance of the public schema may involve the immediate and absolute acceptance of entire systems of ideas at some deep level where they can hardly be challenged. The type of belief in such cases is commensurate with the types of acceptance. For instance, absolute beliefs are adopted under conditions of extreme emotional stress. Sargant has studied this phenomenon (4). He draws a parallel between the shock induced in Pavlov's dogs, religious conversions, and the "brainwashing" of the Chinese communists.

The familiar pathological divisions may be looked at from this perspective. The neurotic is one in whom the conflict between private and public retention schemata has become active. The private schema has challenged the public schema. The struggle has caused a partial withdrawal from external preoccupations; that is why there are often emotional disturbances in such cases, "unfocused anxiety," for instance. The emotions are not unfocused; they are focused on an internal object. There is a substitute equilibrium established between mutually exclusive drives or between appetite and aversion. The anxiety neurotic makes no decision. He is transfixed by an unresolvable conflict, caught in a closed loop, and can only go round and round with it. He is not compulsive, he is enmeshed. There is no refusal to adapt, only an inability.

The psychotic is one in whom the conflict between the private and public schemata has been settled; only the private schema has prevailed over the public schema. The schizophrenic suffers from schematic disorganization, with the dominance of the private schema. The manic depressive suffers from rigid determination by the private schema. The withdrawal from the external world is now complete; there is no more correspondence with reality. Private retention schemata are no longer called upon to withstand the shock of the discovery that they contain beliefs incorporating false propositions. Consistency is still required on which to rest a sense of reality. But the sense of reality can now be satisfied internally. The internal world is the real world for the psychotic, and if he is concerned with the external world at all it is only because he has incorporated it in his own world. He is occupied with maintaining an all-embracing solipsism.

Defects in the cultural circuit may also be responsible for pathological conditions. We have already noted that artifacts often behave in ways not expected or required by their originators but determined instead by their own organization. These may have pathological effects. It is particularly true at the cultural level, when, for instance, occupational diseases assume neurotic proportions.

It may be that in the pathological individual we have the situation of normal sets of inhibitions run wild. It is possible that controls may themselves be inhibited, with irrational behavior as a result. Neurological lesions give rise to the defective display of intentions, and the corresponding reactions represent disorganized actions. Randomization in such a case is equivalent to disorganization. Once more there is a reversion to the primitive chance signals of the infantile nervous system.

Not all pathological conditions are accidental and involuntary, however. Men have succeeded in inventing artifacts which stimulate them to abnormal states. Institutions, such as religion and art, embody rituals and artifacts which produce excessive emotions. Drugs, such as alcohol, opium, mescaline and lysergic acid have similar effects. The necessity for the abnormal is not very well understood, and hence the boundaries of the pathological are confused. It may be that what is called normal in the human rhythm is the crest of a large wave in which the "abnormal" plays a conventional and necessary part as the trough. The pattern may be one of extend-and-adjust rather than of simple maintenance requiring tensions within tolerable limits. The pathological individual is one in whom extension or adjustment is a fixed and frozen state. Examples would be the homicidally inclined paranoid, for extension; and the catatonic schizophrenic, for adjustment. Both ends of the normal rhythm have been pushed to pathological extremes. Actually, a variation is more normal than a persistent condition. It is the fixed personality which exhibits pathological tendencies. The paranoids who think they are Napoleon fall into a familiar pattern. For this reason they are not individually interesting; they concern the therapist intellectually only as a type. More interesting to him would be the mind of Napoleon, of which there has been only one.

THE METHOD OF TRANSFER MATCHING

The theory of therapy can be arrived at deductively from the foregoing account of pathological individuals. If for instance it were conceded to be true that pathology is subjectivity, then therapy would be objectivity. In the case of a subjectively-oriented patient, how is objectivity to be restored?

It would be necessary to reorient the individual toward the external world. We must in fact make the adjustments necessary to reconstruct his equilibrium so that it depends upon a balance between his drive and some external goal: either a material object or an inter-personal relation. How is this to be accomplished?

Therapy at the cultural level is more strongly rational. It has been practiced successfully by depth psychology, and, in the upside down anatomy in which all schemata are held in the unconscious, it consists in the effort to probe by means of a long series of interviews through the conscious defenses of the privately-held schema by reaching past the theorematic beliefs to the axiomatic beliefs on which they rest. For it is only by restoring to consciousness not only the axiomatic beliefs but also the exact emotional occasions on which they were adopted that we can hope to show that the beliefs themselves do not correspond with the reality of the external world.

Another approach, however, is possible. The organization of the schemata as maintained in the pathological individual can be reversed, and the ascendency of the public retention schema over the private restored. Considerable forces will have to be brought into play if the rigid structure guarded by the equilibrium neurotic is to be smashed and the elements reassembled.

The method is called transfer matching, and the steps are as follows. First, the structure and content of the patient's pathological schemata are studied; next this private schema is matched morphologically with a public schema; then some emotional occasion is found for the substitution of public for private schema.

The emotional occasion needs to be a strong one. Electric or chemical shock could be combined with the inculcation of commonly accepted ideas, similar to the way in which an active role for the therapist is often employed in narcoanalysis. It can be assumed that a public retention schema has already carved out channels; it was once accepted by the patient. Therapy of this sort, therefore, would amount to a restoration of familiar habit patterns, like reviving a shattered memory in the midst of familiar surroundings. Tensions can be created by teams of discussants, together with suggestions of personal danger. There is some resemblance here to the forced conversions of communism or to the voluntary revivalist religious conversions, only this time the public schema is the scientific philosophy of truths and facts.

It is curious that, at the present time, shock techniques are employed yet expected to accomplish their therapy though empty of content. The patient is shocked into a state in which anything could be accepted but the method ends there, and he is provided with nothing for acceptance. He is left devoid of suggestion at a stage where he needs most urgently to be informed. Admittedly, preparing a calendar of beliefs suitable for adoption will be a matter of the utmost difficulty. We shall need to discover and perhaps to agree upon a system of propositions comprising the most urgent items which we accept in our own culture, and the problem will be different for every culture. Then there is the technique of input to be worked out; some deliberate procedure for programming the patient.

Perhaps, in the therapeutic session following electroshock, the presentation of the ideas which it is required that the patient shall accept must be made repeatedly, but with as much variety as possible: the same ideas but in different linguistic expressions. A succession of therapists may be necessary, so that in addition to the variety of language there is a variety of voice and intonation as well as of personality. Then, too, teams may be necessary to cover the required temporal span adequate for secure input. Other stimuli during these sessions should be held to a minimum.

Confinement serves to block other channels of expression and hence lends to the situation the added property of displacement behavior. The restoration of the public retention schema and the consequent subordination of private should restore normal discharge functions to their proper channels. Innate behavior patterns peculiar to specific beliefs could find their own paths, and displacement behavior would tend to disappear.

What we are after of course is a reconstituted equilibrium between drive and external goal, and we wish to reverse the substitution which had been made in his case of an equilibrium based on a balanced internal conflict (two goals suspended on a choice point). The problem is how to redirect the drive toward an external goal. No approach can be made in such cases through the reason. But it may be possible to work backward: to so direct action that a will trained by it could strengthen the character.

Therapy somehow needs to provide a shift from an internal to an external focus, and along with it a fixation on the future rather than the past. Degrees of intensity of feeling greater than simple acceptance, such as accompanies the concentrated perception of a particular sense datum, would have to be attached to propositions having some relevance to the future.

The external world upon which the patient is to be directed consists in many concentric circles. There is the available environment which the patient himself could immediately affect and which for pathological reasons he supposes is all that affects him. Freud was concerned with an externalization of the patient's focus upon this world. Adler had a somewhat broader conception, and wished to focus the patient not upon what is but what ought to be—upon the ideal. Yet this ideal was somehow conceived in attainable terms, and so the patient was given a workable goal if a short-lived one. But there is a wider external world, and we are immersed in it. In the conception being advanced here, the external focus is the world, all of it. Hence the final ambition in therapy is what we might for want of a better word call philosophical feelings, feelings which carry with them cosmic assurances, the assurances that any legitimate thing, however small, is some part of the whole world, and that consequently it will be well with us.

Beliefs feel good and strong beliefs feel better. It becomes a question, then, of how much the neurological equilibrium relies upon the feelings. The most compelling feelings are those called out by particular rational systems. On this basis rest all the organized world religions and political systems. If a method can be provided for substituting in the next stage of abstraction a feeling for reason as such, the effect will be overwhelming; there is no emotion more powerful than the emotion of reason. It takes a strong stomach to live on the hard fare which reason can provide when beliefs are limited to logic and fact, but in the long run a healthier individual is bound to result.

CHAPTER 4

BIOSOCIAL ADAPTATION AND
MENTAL ILLNESS

H UMAN beings are biological organisms but they live in the immediate environment of a material world containing other organisms and physical objects. Culture is part of this environment, and human beings are influenced by it no less than by other parts. They are under the repeated necessity of adjusting themselves to their total environment, and such an adjustment over a considerable period consists in a kind of biological adaptation. The nature of such adaptation has been studied since Darwin, and is continuing to be studied by a host of anthropologists, sociologists, archaeologists and social psychologists. Yet in some curious fashion, human evolution and the evolution of human culture have been studied side by side, but always separately. They have not been related in any intimate way nor their interactions pursued in any advanced situations. Much remains to be done in this direction. One such effort lies along pathological lines; it can be shown how biological adaptation can lead to mental illness.

It would not take much to show that such separation defeats the understanding of evolution so far as it affects human beings. For evolution involves an adaptation to the environment but also a struggle toward greater complexity: not mere adaptation, for in this way the evolution of more complex organizations could never be explained. The problem for any organization is, how to grow in complexity within the limits set by the environment, and the solution discovered by organisms is to use the environment in or-

55

der to take advantage of the environment. When this effort fails in individual cases, it does so to the disorganization of the individual and pathology results. The resulting pathology is conventional in the sense that the failures are classifiable because of the dominance of similarities over differences in individual cases.

The aim of this study, then, is to analyze the relations between mental illness and culture as such, on the ground that the former is the price that to some extent has been paid for the latter. The effect of the evolution of cultures is more fundamental than the accultural stress brought about by the conflict of cultures or by the imposition of one culture upon another (14).

Cultures make it possible to be human but at the same time impose stresses upon the individual. The alteration of material objects through human agency, whether weapons made by chipping, game cooked by fire, or caves decorated for shelters, are methods by which man has learned to stimulate himself. Every technological advance is not only a new way of getting something objective accomplished but also a fresh means of self-stimulation. And the stimulation in turn leads to novel responses.

Culture begins early in human history. The transition to bipedalism of the quadrupedal, stone-throwing, man-apes was the result of the use of tools, more specifically of small stones as weapons (20). In the caves which yield Australopithicine remains pebble tools made of stone from other sites are often found. Suffice to say that bipedalism, with all its drastic consequences, was only the beginning. There seem to be reasons for supposing that bipedalism, which set man free to use his hands, was responsible also for speech and so for much of human culture. Handedness is closely related to speech in the cortical areas in which both are represented (12). What we are faced with now is the fact that such stimulation when accelerated has a tendency to exceed tolerable limits. Rapid change, the swift transition to new conditions, surrounded by new instruments which are hardly understood, constitutes a strain and is therefore conducive to mental illness. Man provides himself with his own environment, and inadvertently produces his own diseases.

The influence of man on his development continues still; not only the adjustment of life to the capital city, with its material objects and symbolic communications, but also such recent—and radical—changes as oral contraceptives, hormones, space flight, and other inventions. What further biological modifications will result from the new application by man of scientific discoveries upon himself? It is difficult to predict anything except that they will be extensive. And, it is safe to add, they will generate their own types of mental diseases.

There seems to be some evidence that as the cultural content changes, the structure of mental disease changes also. Culture is found in the content. Obsessive-compulsive neuroses, fear and anxiety states, would be the same whether found in China, among American Indians, or in the western society, but the content of course would vary depending upon the culture. Chinese, American Indian and western mental diseases are not the same (14). The extent to which mental diseases spread is a function of the degree of stress which a particular culture imposes upon its members; prevalence therefore could vary when variety did not. The prevalence of mental disease may result from the amount of acceleration involved in a culture's progress.

By means of the complex cultures of the modern world, man has constructed his own environment. In the industrial cultures which applied science has brought into being, it is rare for an individual to encounter and to be stimulated by anything except material objects which have been altered through human agency. The elements comprising the non-human environment have receded respectably into the background, where they are hardly noticed. Consider for a moment what this means. It means that in the available environment of the human individual, the man-altered world small though it be takes precedence over the remainder of the cosmic universe. Who in a city can see the stars? Where is the sense of the enormity of existence to be acquired, except perhaps through a session with the arts or a study of the sciences? But this is not ordinarily the way in which ordinary people occupy themselves. Making a living usually requires that hour to hour occupations be with the material elements of a culture: keeping accounting books, selling shirts, operating a drilling machine or working on an assembly line. For the purposes pertinent here, economic status makes no difference; playing golf or cutting coupons are also ways of keeping occupied with the material elements of a culture. These facts are significant in their effects upon individual man. The nature of the environment, whether it consists in a world untouched by humans, or a man-fashioned material culture, makes a difference to individual personality. For personality depends upon the interaction between the environment and slight differences in inborn nervous function (19, pp. 377–391).

The effect of living almost entirely in an artificial environment has hardly been understood and rarely studied. For it is not merely the environment which is for man culture-bound but also man himself. Consider for instance the acquisition of knowledge, skills and feelings. The knowledge is always abstract, and abstractions have to be discriminated chiefly from among the available artifacts or culture-objects; the skills are new ways of behavior, that is to say, new ways of affecting artifacts; and even the feelings, which have preserved so sacrosanct a subjective classification, are now understood to be in many ways learned. Training in the appreciation of art is capable of changing tastes and increasing feelings.

Genetically speaking, the human personality has been a difficult thing to construct and maintain. It might aid us in the understanding of personality if we were to consider its construction and maintenance separately.

First, then, as to the construction of the personality. A most enlightening account has been given by Piaget of the development of the child. We might appeal to his example of the development of thought as an instance of construction (15). The psychological development of the individual begins only when past experiences exercise an effect upon present behavior; that is to say, when experience is interpreted in terms of organized schemata. Experience is subjected to a developmental process of assimilation and organization of schemata. And the schemata themselves have grown up as products of experience. Thoughts, like images, are imitations of an external reality, which is the world. Thus arise the ideas of objectivity and of logical necessity. Genetically, thought is a learned structure, the elements of which come from the attempt to assemble internally images of objects experienced as external. The construction of the personality requires, then, both a system of thought and continuous learning from experience. The development from child to adult is a gradual process of objectivization. This is true not only in the opinion of the child psychologists, such as Piaget, but in that of the neurophysiologists as well, such as Gellhorn. In noting that the present environment interacts with the schemata organized in the past, it should not be forgotten that the contents of the frames of reference, which are the schemata, are themselves products of experience, of interaction with the environment, and are in no sense *a priori* except in the determination that the products of experience are bound to be organized if they are to influence behavior integrally. Gellhorn has pointed out that at least in our own minds our perceptions are parts of the objects and not parts of our sense organs (6, pp. 421–22).

The schemata, which are structures of the contents of memory, are fixed, whereas experience is a flowing process. The fixed nature of memory has impressed investigators from Freud to W. R. Russell. Much of Freud's theory and psychotherapy hangs upon the indelible nature of early imprinting. Russell supposes that it is part of the activity of the central nervous system to maintain the contents of memory intact through the spontaneous discharge of the nerve cells (17, p. 16). Contrast this inflexibility with the inherent flux in the data of experience. No wonder that equilibrium under such circumstances is hard to maintain and requires continual adaptation. Assimilating new knowledge to a store already maintained is a business of stumbling from compromise to compromise, a rolling readjustment of beliefs about the external world, where the more basic are the more fixed and the less basic the more easily disturbed. In this way, experience plays over the surface of knowledge without stirring the deeper portions—at least not so easily.

It would seem that the conditions necessary for consciousness and equilibrium differ; the novelty essential for the former constitutes a threat to the latter. They can be reconciled, but only by means of an adjustment to inquiry. The continual alert which the repeated encounter with surprises calls for continues consciousness but the balance depends upon an endless supply of the unexpected. Thus the personality derives from an origin in the function of searching.

The maintenance of the personality proceeds imperceptibly from its construction. Consciousness requires novelty in continuous input, but against a background of equilibrium. Every novelty threatens equilibrium and every habituation reinforces it. When the level of habituation is too low, security is challenged. The entire construction is thereby given up as presenting a hopelessly impossible adjustment. But when novelty is missing, consciousness disappears, for the central nervous system does not respond to monotonous stimuli (2).

Under the circumstances, maintenance neurophysiologically requires a graded response, which is in fact what exists. We owe to Magoun and others the concept of the graded response, and the knowledge that the negative feedback loop within the nervous system extends to the environment (10, pp. 70, 73). The grading is done by the reticular formation of the brain, and it operates both upward and downward (11, p. 115); upward to the cortex and downward to the external stimuli (3, p. 378). The brain stem controls not only the erosion of information but also the reception of additional information (9, p. 378).

Extending the feedback loop to the environment involves a specificity of stimulus which was not necessary when the stimulus was unspecified. This was the case, for instance, under the stimulus-response mechanism of the behaviorists. There it was the response which was important; the stimulus triggered a process in which it was no longer needed. Now, however, the circuit returns to the stimulus and so its singular properties, and their consequent changes, must remain part of the consideration. An all-or-nothing response is barely related to the stimulus and most certainly loses contact with the stimulus; a graded response remains in continual contact with it.

If we were to take full advantage of these two sets of data: the need for both novelty and habituation on the one hand, and the graded response on the other, we should see that the two-valued logic is inadequate for dealing with practical problems of any considerable degree of complexity. It has been emphasized often enough in recent decades that the law of excluded middle does not apply to the concrete particulars of actual existence. Except in logic, it is simply not the case that anything must be either A or non-A.

A question, for instance, may suggest not an answer but a range of answers. If someone were to ask, "Will there be a war this year?" the suggested answers might be "yes," "no," "perhaps," or "What should we consider a war?" For either there will be a war or peace will continue or we will not be sure whether there will be a war or peace will continue or there will be a "cold war" or a hot peace.

Statistical expressions allowing for freedom of adjustment are required by the objectivization of thought processes (Piaget) and of the sense perceptions (Gellhorn). It comes to this, that what is produced by the environment and continues to react with the environment belongs intrinsically to the environment. But by what logic is such a process to be analyzed?

If we take the two-valued logic, then in the organism the synapse is the control mechanism. It can allow an impulse from receptor to effector or not (7, p. 18). The analogy is the digital computer. But for the graded response the analogy is the analog computer. And the logic will have to be non-deductive and non-linear. Von Neumann once pointed out that while logic received credit as the foundations of mathematics, it was combinatorial and thus far lay at the foundations only of algebra and geometry (18, p. 16). What was needed, he thought, was a logic for mathematical analysis, involving the concepts of continuity and able to deal with real and complex numbers. Since analysis was the most advanced part of mathematics, logic was lagging sadly behind.

There are two prospects in logic and mathematics which may offer some help. One is the axiomatization of probability theory (8) and the other the many-valued logics (16). Further, there are glimpses of the possibility of non-deductive logical systems, structures defined by the relations existing between their elements. Could a logic and a mathematics be devised to take care of qualities, of multiple causation and multiple effects, and to provide for the breadth that there is to some concepts? These questions may have to be answered constructively before it will be possible to analyze nervous nets.

If novelty is a component of input necessary for the maintenance of consciousness, then the mathematics requisite for its analysis remains to be discovered. But novelty is not altogether an offering of the environment; it requires active discrimination and search. The activity consists in the search for the information required to satisfy curiosity. The stimuli, as Deutsch insists, end the response rather than begin it (4). When we have the information we shut off the search. But since it is curiosity which discovers novelty, curiosity is needed for survival.

For early man, the dangers from the environment furnished the necessary stimulus of novelty. But now those dangers have been substantially reduced as man has made tremendous gains in the control of the environment. He has made the available environment, that part of it which lies within his reach, to a great extent familiar and his own. In place of danger, safety; in place of novelty, however, ignorance and bafflement. Regimentation accompanies enormous increases in population, and necessary controls are introduced as a consequence. Faceless man emerges (13); personality-wise, the elimination of differences leads to a conformity which is repetitious and death-like. The novelty of forms has been replaced with mere formal novelty. We no longer understand the mechanisms operating our stimuli, but we count on their novelty being held within severe limits. The psychological stimulation approaches zero and only the physical impact remains.

The remaining dangers are chiefly those accounted for by man himself; efficiency in war. It operates to slow down the processes which make progress possible: constructive novelty and variety. As opposed to this there is the acceleration of evolution brought about by the rapidity of development of the artificial environment. There is something new in the world, namely, the extent to which man is able to change his environment. The attempt to understand this development has led to one of the most serious errors. It is supposed by some thinkers, for instance, that because man can now change his environment, it can no longer change him, and that as a consequence the process of organic evolution has been brought to a halt (5).

From the data, exactly the opposite would appear to be true. We have noted at the outset of this chapter the theory that the invention of tools was responsible for bipedalism. This was roughly some million years ago. The situation in this regard has not changed; it has accelerated. The more complex the tools, the more radical the change in tool-users. More complex tools call for more complex human adaptation. It is not only the tools which change but ourselves; and if the rate is somewhat slower than can be detectable in recorded time, which is after all some forty-five hundred years, a mere fraction of human history, the dramatic consequences are not reduced appreciably thereby. If stone tools can change man from the career determined by his ape-like posture to the bipedalism which leaves the hands free, what influences are now being exerted upon his descendants by the invention of industrialism, technology and applied science, by automation, for instance, and by computers?

An accelerated evolution is inherent in the effects of a rapidly changing cultural environment. It is no longer a question of cumulative accretions of change in a relatively fixed environment. But there is a still further development which may prove to be of great significance. There is a growing dependence of human beings on the complexities of technology. Although technology does provide a greater degree of perfection of services, there is a comparative growth of lack of understanding. Apart from a few applied physicists and engineers, the population has not been able to keep up with the effectiveness of the complexity of human inventions. A few men are responsible for the machines most men cannot understand. The machines, moreover, exceed human powers; they are more quick in their mental processes, more capable in their memory, more efficient in their operation. Collectively, we have invented them and not they us; but, like all primitive tools, they can do things that we cannot do except build them to do it. An arrow can fell an animal that runners could not catch, but a computer can make calculations in a very few minutes that would take mathematicians weeks. The complexity has increased while the principle has remained the same. Yet the increase has achieved enormous and challenging proportions. What will the machines do to us, and what will our lack of understanding of them cost us?

Perhaps there has been something of a cost already. The processes conditioning life in the available environment (the mesocosm) are now set for it by the extra-mesocosmic forays into the world of the very small, the microcosm, as made available by electron microscopes, for example, and the world of the very large, the macrocosm, as made available by radio and optical telescopes, for example. Operations in industry are currently performed at high speeds, at high temperatures, and with mathematical complexity.

The fact is that human beings never have accepted their role as inquirers. They have sought through discovery to escape from the continual pressure of inquiry. Running through every one of the four grand routes of inquiry: art, religion, philosophy and science, after their assistance in the struggle for the satisfaction of basic tissue needs, is the effort to get something established, to find permanent answers to ultimate questions, answers which will dictate fixed ways of behavior, so that human life can become the following of a set of ritual performances as reliable as the phenomena of non-human nature, the cycle of the seasons, for instance, or the phases of the moon. All institutions offer such promises, like governments and churches which outlast many generations. Yet inevitably these, too, must fail; for there is nothing eternal known in its character of difference, and little recurrent except the forms of change. Thus every established culture imposes a strain upon its acceptance, and elicits a rebellion by its very persistence: equilibrium must be sacrificed to consciousness and institutions to novelty, if human life is to survive and complexity increase. Neither the death-like repetition of responses nor the challenge of full novelty can be altogether accepted, and human life vacillates between rebellions against both.

Just now, in western culture, we are in the midst of a period of rapid change, and the human recoil has already begun, the revolt of the masses is subtly manifest in the weakest and most ill-equipped for adjustment and adaptation, the mentally ill. We note fear, suspicion, distrust, resentment, aggression and withdrawal. It is fairly well known that all persons share the difficulties of the schizophrenic, only in him they are reactivated and allowed to become central. Brain malformations or injuries apart, there is manifest deterioration, not an adjustment to lower mental levels, but instead a progressive regression to lower and lower mechanisms (1, p. 419).

With his artificial environment man has scored enormous gains over the non-human environment, but in so doing he has also produced the mental diseases. Along with the environment of machines and against a background of buildings and the material components of institutions, man has estranged himself from the elements which he himself has provided. Such alienation demands actions appropriate to it, and these result in the psychoses. The psychotic struggles to return (paranoid aggression), accepts a partial diremption (paranoia), settles for a complete separation (paranoid delusional systems), refuses to face the problem, preferring to keep it in suspension (catatonic schizophrenia), or alternates between the effort to return and ultimate rejection (manic-depressive psychosis). Culture, in a word, precipitates mental illness.

These are the mentally ill, and most of them can be counted as the victims of a cultural advance which is too rapid to sustain. The rest of the population struggles on, either accepting the challenges as those to be encountered in the normal course of affairs or suffering under extreme tensions. It is well known that only a small percentage of the mentally ill are in hospitals or are under the care of psychiatrists. The larger question of whether modern culture is too complex and constitutes too severe an adjustment or an adaptation can be successfully made is not yet answerable. The history of human progress is a dialectic, not a helix; it can be counted on to oscillate toward a gradual advance but not necessarily to make steady and continual progress.

A contributing factor may lie in the direction of preventive psychiatry. A very much larger social role for the psychiatrist may be a possibility. Instead of aiding the victims of alienation resulting from rapid cultural advance, the psychiatrist may be called on to anticipate the maladjustments which must follow a major cultural advance and devise the preventive practices appropriate to any maladaptation they may occasion. Psychiatry since Freud has operated mainly at the institutional level, and chiefly one institution at that: the family. But as the institutions shift among themselves within a culture, some which have been considered basic drop down in the hierarchy of institutions while others rise. We should expect, for instance, that in China, where the family as a basic institution is being supplanted by the state and by economics, the illnesses would take a different and very unFreud-like form. Consider for example what happened in the United States in the backwash of the 1929 economic depression. Many men in the vigorous years of their manhood temporarily became sexually impotent as the result of the loss of their fortunes.

If psychiatry can keep abreast of cultural progress with an appropriate psychological theory, the role of the psychiatrist may well be to insure a biological adaptation that will prevent mental illness. This is at the present time no more than a hope for the future. Not enough is yet known about social forces, human culture or the nature of brain pathology, to say nothing of the relations between them.

CHAPTER 5

ECOLOGICAL FACTORS IN
HUMAN MALADAPTATIONS

1

THE aim of this chapter is to continue the study of pathological effects of the human ecological situation interpreted as the relation of individuals to cultures. Individual symptoms in social conditioning are to be interpreted as integrative level phenomena. The largest part of the external world, the astronomical domain of the macrocosm, for instance, exists at integrative levels lower than the human. There may be life on other planets, but there are more planets than are inhabited, to say nothing of uninhabitable stars, vast clouds of hydrogen gas. Even on our own planet, while exploration extends within the crust and into the ionosphere, life can be sustained for any length of time and in any numbers only on the surface. But at the human level the nonhuman areas are represented symbolically and so play a role *in absentia*. We shall consider further what happens to the representation of absent objects.

We begin with the prospect of the external world from the perspective of the human individual. It is a vast panorama of shuffled up materials, statistically more profuse at lower integrative levels. And this is true even for that small segment of the environment which is the available environment or mesocosm. Man lives in the "mesocosm," a middle world between two other worlds which he can explore but in which he cannot live: the world of the very small: the microcosm, and the world of the very large: the macrocosm. Within the mesocosm a bewildering array of stimuli furnish the contents of the continual input to which the individual is subjected. The efficacy of positive responses can only follow the learning of "the insignificance of all irrelevant stimuli" (7, p. 320).

The environment extends, then, beyond the reach of the individual; but within his reach it contains the ingredients to satisfy tissue needs in varying degrees. We shall not attempt here to deal with all of these (12, p. 220). His most pressing need, the need for survival, is met with the proper exercise of the avoidance response, and along with this no doubt go all varieties of aversion: fear, aggression, and flight. But with the needs for feeding and breeding, tension arises. Conventional types of thanatophobia are obscured by the more pressing search for food and mate, which are, respectively, less common than the ground he must have under his feet and the air he must breathe into his lungs. Muscle tonus and the oxygen supply take care of themselves; but hunger and sex cravings require more concentration. The constant foraging and courting constitute pressures, and when children are the outcome of the latter, it only increases the pressure on the former.

Thus the individual is driven back to the consideration of how these needs can be anticipated and perhaps met with a long-term supply. To escape the tyranny of the immediate environment, it is necessary to discover how to anticipate future tissue needs and to store up satisfactions to meet them. Communication with others having the same problems becomes urgent, for the successful outcome of such discovery requires the execution of tasks which do not lie within the range of the powers of the individual: hunting large animals, planting, protecting and harvesting vast crops. The entire enterprise, planned for the future, is a way of dealing with absent objects (6) in the general terms of a colloquial language. Inevitably, the relationship between these need-satisfactions is discerned, and curiosity aroused. The individual takes off in search of facts and causes.

It is important to notice, however, that a drastic reversal has taken place, one so subtle as to go almost unnoticed and yet so far-reaching as to constitute another stage in biological evolution. The proposition that:

All inquiries are conducted for the sake of
maintaining existence,

has been converted to the proposition that

All existence is maintained for the sake of
conducting inquiries.

Let us pause at this point to consider some of the consequences
of the conversion.

In the first place, we are of course talking about living propositions, propositions as exemplified in practice, not about the natural history of human thoughts. Men once went where their curiosity led them for the purpose of survival; now they endeavor to
survive in order to go where their curiosity leads them. The turn
has been called not by the recognition of it in discourse but by the
events themselves.

In the second place, such a reversal plays havoc with the drives
toward the satisfaction of such tissue needs. The brain once occupied a subordinate role, being subservient to stomach and gonads.
Now stomach and gonads function in order that there shall be a
continuity of activity for the brain. But there is a further dislocation; for bits of the environment are internalized by the stomach
and gonads, but the larger environment is contacted by the brain.

Evolutionary development is inverse to morphological dependence (3). The higher centers, such as the frontal lobes, were
late arrivals on the phylogenetic scene; but on the other hand,
the brain depends upon the other organs for its survival, and
within the brain the higher centers depend upon the lower. For
instance, circulation throughout the brain depends upon the
proper blood pressure; and a continual fall in the blood sugar
would produce at first loss of consciousness (with involvement of
the frontal lobes), next convulsions (the cerebellum) and finally
respiration difficulties (the medulla) and death.

Finally, due to the external nature of the aim of inquiry, material objects are altered in the course of it. Inquiry involves
analysis, but it also leads to synthesis: social groups are formed
and their organization established, tools are designed and techniques devised, and both are copied, and structures are erected

and inherited. The accumulation achievement replaces the continuity of conditions. In place of the mere repetition of behavior by the successive generations, there is a construction of culture.

As for the individual, the knowledge of what exists now becomes the object of his search. He has turned into the creature who survives in order to inquire, erecting quasi-permanent answers into institutions, social relations operating, so to speak, in a neurological setting. For now the dependence of his organism upon the environment can be analyzed into one of dependence of the balance between homeostasis and the brain stem reticular activity. He bears the scars of his experience as collections of engrams, organized into explanatory beliefs: retention schemata both private and public. Thus equipped, he supplements the neurological homeostasis with a cultural homeostasis extended to include material objects. Such objects usually have the character of artifacts, because altered through human agency. His encounter with the environment in search of tissue-need satisfactions has resulted in an equilibrium between the retention schemata and the civilized external world. The continual interchange has been widely recognized; for it is acknowledged that "the cerebral instrument breaks down with zero input" (13, p. 378) but on the other hand breaks down also when it is no longer able to sustain contradictions without diremption. It is the latter variety we have largely to deal with in psychopathology. Being human means sustaining private conflicts, and being social means sustaining public conflicts (as within and between retention schemata). The neurotic is threatened by diremption and the psychotic has succumbed to it.

2

Technological cultures, as products of the attempt to solve the long-term supply problem necessary for survival, themselves raise survival problems by bringing into play stresses of a peculiar type. In simpler cultures, in our own culture, too, in fact as late as the early nineteenth century, the individual was constantly subjected to external stresses and internal strains. Inter-personal relations, customs, institutions, with their conflicts and struggles, always exist. But the external stresses were limited to social struggles and the internal to the usual fear of death. In the complex cultures brought about more lately by the combination of the applications of science and industrial technology, a cultural homeostasis becomes more difficult to achieve and maintain. There are, of course, many psychoses to which youth is susceptible, such as hebephrenic schizophrenia and psychopathic personality. But the aged are more susceptible, and in 1960 in the United States it was true that "one out of every three beds in public mental hospitals is occupied by a person sixty-five or older" (8). Rapid social change erodes the ground on which such a homeostasis could rest.

But there are worse difficulties. The chief feature of the scientifico-industrial culture which technology has developed is its abstractness. Forays into the microcosm and macrocosm have been successful. Men have returned with their scientific spoils, and the result is to change the character of the mesocosm, which now contains artifactual inhabitants seldom understood by few nonspecialists, with their effects which are less understood still. The average individual lives for the first time in a world populated with material objects and procedures he does not understand and is perhaps incapable of grasping. He drives a car but does not fully understand the principle of the internal combustion engine; he operates a television set but does not comprehend the principle of the vacuum tube; he engages in business but does not understand the modern complexities of banking; he ingests vitamin capsules or antibiotics without the slightest glimmer of how they were constructed or of what they do. He is both benefactor and recipient of inquiries predicated on the search for a solution to the long-term supply of basic tissue-needs conducted at the level of the inexhaustible tissue-need of inquiry, and yet he remains in ignorance. And at this level he is expected to adjust. The scientifico-industrial culture like all other cultures, resulted from human behavior; but now the capital city, which is one result, itself provides the new conditions to which it becomes necessary for men once again to adapt. This time they have provided themselves with the stimuli as well as the responses. They have invented their own environment.

Only, as it turns out, they have done so without anticipating and estimating the prospects and costs of adjustment. The mesocosm is for the first time a world of their own devising yet it now develops that they did not figure it closely enough. The immediate environment is an altogether artificial environment. They have made themselves a world in which to live without considering just what it would mean to live in it. If it is true that the dependence of the organism upon its environment extends all the way from simple cell-division and the acid-alkalinity balance to the contents of excretions and the metabolic interchange, then what adjustments in body structure will be required for survival in the new social world? To live in the mesocosm now means to have all the stimulation of the receptors coming from the cultural environment. The ears are assailed by man-made sounds, from street noises to jazz. Few are able to escape from the roar of the traffic of some city. The eyes are continually in contact with artifacts. What with the skyscrapers, the obscuring city lights by night and the smog by day, the sky is hardly ever visible, and there is no incentive to view it. The nose is assailed by odors artificially produced, from the smell of asphalt and inhabited interiors to that of perfumes. Everything except artifacts is out of reach so that the sense of touch is equally confined. There are few foods ingested that have not been altered by the process of manufacture in some way, and thus even taste is artificially conditioned. Finally, even the muscle sense is stimulated by the activity of the muscles in exertion against artifacts, moving them about or altering their shape.

All of this is bound to have serious biological repercussions. Anatomical development over its long history has been shown to be a matter of adaptation through natural selection. It is assumed that this process accounts, for instance, for the adjustment of the respiratory system to the contents of the atmosphere, of the muscular system to the geosphere, of the digestive system to the biosphere, and of the nervous system to human society (the "sociosphere").

Now in maladaptive behavior, there is usually phyletic extinction; but it is a peculiar feature of human society that it endeavors to bring the victims along. This has the double merit of helping them and of learning from the causes of their predicament how healthier specimens may better adapt and so survive. Space medicine is a recent development intended to study how to provide for extraordinary conditions, stresses, for instance, brought about by gravity increases and by enormous accelerations in speed. But what is not equally recognized is that there are, so to speak, no ordinary conditions. The life expectancy has been extended and the buffeting multiplied.

Look at the individual from the point of view of the cultural environment in which he is presently immersed. See him as the recipient of stimuli projected from artifacts. He shaves with an electric razor, rides in a subway, rises in an elevator, operates a typewriter or a high speed computer, while his wife does the washing in a machine designed for the purpose, cooks on an electric grille and waits for his return to relax with the radio. They live in a world populated by little motors which they do not understand and which far outnumber them. But this is an empirical area and there is an experimental science which investigates it. The domain is that of social psychology, which is the study not of social groups and their behavior but of the modification of individuals by institutions and cultures.

The common world is a physical, chemical and biological world. The social world is a selection made by the alternation of responses to environmental stimuli in the form of constructions: tools, symbolic communication systems, institutions, cultures. Here the group decides, though not as a group but rather as individuals in whom the group participates (2).

The gap between cultural artifact and psychological individual is the one the neurological circuit has to bridge. The issue always turns on whether the diversity of organic reactions can be stretched to cope with the complexity of conditions produced by the scientifico-industrial culture. One method is to extend technological assistance to the various organs: spectacles for the eyes, magnifying devices for the ears, prosthetic devices for the limbs, and so on. We see the problem more clearly in the case of a man who operates his television set with an artificial hand, watches it through corrective glasses, and listens to it by means of a hearing aid. These mechanical extensions to the receptors and affectors are in many ways quite satisfactory; and although they contribute toward enlisting the individual in the culture in a way calculated to render

him an irreversible dependent, they also help to stave off the reactions in which the breakdown of functions would otherwise
occur.

We may, however, do well to consider a set of reactions in
which breakdown does occur. A formidable one concerns language. An early and well marked mental defect is the loss of the
ability to deal with abstractions. This may take one of two forms:
either the individual loses the ability to abstract, or he loses the
ability to control certain of his abstractions.

Inability to abstract is a well known maturational defect, but
sensory and motor disturbances are often accompanied by symbolic deficiencies. Patients with brain injuries in the general re-
gion of Broca's area, the third left frontal convolution, avoid abstractions in favor of concrete terms; they cannot understand
classes and class relationships. Aphasia is manifested by (among
other symptoms) a lowered capacity for abstract thought, a de-
ficiency shared by psychopathic personalities.

If the loss of the ability to abstract characterizes one type of
mental disease, the loss of the ability to control abstractions
characterizes another. There are at least two varieties, exemplified by the hebephrenic and the paranoid schizophrenic. In the
former case, we have the spectacle of displacement into a fan-
tastic private language from the failure to participate in conven-
tionally established abstractions. In the latter case, the phenomenon is one of uncontrolled conventional generalization. The
avoidance posture of the paranoid compels him to select particular
threats in his environment, or to mistake neutral or friendly elements for threats. As the response of rage is made to the stimulus
of fear, the inductions of the paranoid proliferate indiscrimi-
nately. " 'This man is against me' implies 'All men are against
me' implies 'I am being persecuted.' " The organization of the
antipathy of all men is unwarrantedly assumed in this enthy-
meme.

Neurotic behavior is maladaptive behavior; psychotic behavior
marks the retention of maladaptive habits, their establishment as
a personal but less than provisional security. The motivation of
survival has replaced the need of inquiry, a distinct regression.
At the same time, an autistic adjustment is not an acceptable set-

tlement, for it decreases the external stresses at the cost of increasing the internal strains. Hence the prevalence of suicidally inclined patients in mental hospitals.

There is, as Walter has pointed out, only one chaos (13, p. 378). The chaotic world of the psychotic is to that extent a common world. But there are many types of order. The approximation to the condition of chaos on the part of the stimulus-world is an approach to zero input. The world of the hebephrenic is a chaotic world from which stimuli have been held to a minimum, and as a consequence the activity of the higher centers of his nervous system no longer constitutes a learning process. External order, in short, is a condition of proper functioning for the organism, and external order can be apprehended only through the abstract symbols of a technique of communication, which is to say, through a language.

The history of the organism which must be taken into account in explaining its behavior does not mean references to the past but to those alterations in the organism made in the past but existing in the present, alterations such as the posited engrams and the more manifest habitual behavior patterns. Unfortunately for the stressed individual, these include conflicting schemata: the public retention schema containing the ideals of social behavior, as taught in early years by parents, teachers and textbooks, and the statements of public officials; and the private retention schema containing the hard facts as personal experience has revealed them: as for instance the cutting edge of the selfishness or the dishonesty of others, bitter disappointments, secret but forbidden enjoyments, short turns to success. In other words, as the two types of schemata collide, the conditions for private conflict are laid down early and well. They insure that the individual will have the task of integrating his own conflicting schemata before adapting to the alien world of his culture's devising. If he fails to succeed in this, he has little choice but to subside to lower integrative levels; lower organisms are not capable of sustaining diverse retention schemata, and psychotics no longer undertake to do so.

The exceptions, perhaps, are sufferers from paranoia, who keep the external world separate from their delusional systems, and the psychopathic personalities who persist in expecting agreement from the external world for theirs. The high order of logical structure retained in paranoia for the delusional system is spread by the psychopathic personality thinly over the connections between his own goal-seeking and the objective facts. Both are victims of atrophy of the feelings, and lack all empathetic reactions. Something of this sort is suggested by the discovery of the dysfunction of the autonomic system in psychotic individuals (9) but the difficulty is in all likelihood more widespread.

Psychotics are quite capable of dealing with artifacts, but the social contacts have been cut at the level of inter-personal relations. What does this mean, except that the psychotic denies an interaction and looks for affects that flow in one direction only? He can take, but he is in no position to give.

3

In the first part of this chapter were set forth some of the stages in the process whereby cultures have developed out of the attempts to anticipate and prepare for the satisfaction of future basic tissue needs. We saw how the brain, which came to the fore in this effort to help feeding and breeding, ended by taking precedence over them; so that whereas it had existed for them they now had come to exist for it. This new adjustment led to a species of human maladaptation. In the second part of the chapter it was shown how, in the attempt to live in the environment brought about by the cultures they have produced, men have tended to break down. Psychoneuroses and psychoses are the results of the stresses of complex scientifico-industrial cultures.

Now, then, it will be necessary to address ourselves to the solution of problems raised by the existence of culture as the human environment. Cultures are not new and the individual strains of living in them are not new, either. But in earlier cultures, the cultural environment was a small part of the available environment. In the scientifico-industrial cultures it begins to encroach strongly. Thus it raises problems which if not altogether novel present difficulties to a degree that amounts to a major crisis. What, if anything, can be done about it?

We may perhaps begin the discussion of this question by taking a page from the science of neurology. There we find two conflicting conditions. It seems that for the normal functioning of the human organism both the constancy of the external environment and differences in stimulation are required. Perception appears to hang upon the former and consciousness upon the latter.

Perception is of a physical world independent of the observer, a world which is stable, rigid, solid and orderly in a way which, as Gibson says, gives "objectivity to our experience" and makes perception itself possible (5, pp. 186-7, 230). For perception— in this case visual perception—is constructed to encounter such conditions and relies upon finding them. Gellhorn goes so far as to assert that "the constancy of the external environment is a cortical function" (4), without which the individual would neither be suitably oriented nor able to act purposively.

That consciousness would not be possible without differences in the objective field of consciousness has been shown by experiment (1, pp. 196, 222). Monotonously repeated stimuli lead to sleep. The inner ear, which is so sensitive to any irregular forces, does not react at all to uniform motion. Order among stimuli is relaxing. Hypnotism relies heavily upon this effect, and anyone who has driven a car for hours over a straight and level road can testify to its truth. The uniformity of perfect order or of chaos allows for no stimuli at all, and without the continuous input of diverse stimuli there is no consciousness.

How, then, is this paradox to be related to the problem of resolving the psychopathological strains which complex cultures impose upon their individual members? The next step is to discover the optimal pragmatic set of conditions under which cultures can be maintained with their immense benefits but without serious damage to the individual. How much progress in cultures can the individual support? There are, once again, two parts to this question. There is the problem of the internal dislocation in the individual: the distortion of the private retention schema by the public. And there is the problem of the external dislocation of the culture: the distortion of the institutional structure by the ascendency of a particular institution.

Both problems resolve themselves into one again when we consider that the state of the culture is operant in both cases with equal effectiveness. For the internal dislocation of the individual depends upon the character of the cultural stimuli to which he is subjected, and the institutional state of the culture depends upon his own sense of what institutions are most important in conducting inquiries. Thus at the present time science is the crucial institution; it offers not only to feed the basic tissue need of pure inquiry but also to further the long term supply of satisfactions for the survival needs. As a consequence the rapid rate of change in fundamental theory brought about by the new conceptions of matter and of the cosmos has compelled a revision of the public retention schema, while technological advances have improved the food supply, both as to quantity and quality, increased the safety of birth-control and provided efficient contraceptives.

However, these changes have been brought about at a rapid rate, and the resultant challenge to the homeostasis of the individual is alarming. Too much and too frequent stimulation has its price. It is possible to over-stimulate, with a result not unlike the absence of all stimulation. To quote an athletic director, "these ailments are continuous—always something new" (10). The life expectancy has been dramatically extended but so has the prevalence of mental illness. The enormous rise in the population of our mental hospitals in recent years, together with the immense number of psychoneurotics and even psychotics who are able to maintain themselves on a precarious balance outside, is well known.

At this point, it seems impossible to turn the clock back. The cerebral development, and in particular the development of the frontal lobes, prohibits the mere existence of man at the monotonous level at which no change and progress in living conditions prevails. The cerebrum assures the continuance of inquiry whereas the more fundamental mechanisms of the reticular formation of the brain stem require a constancy of the external environment. From the stimulus end, the cultures we inherit make more complex inquiry possible but also block them out by vested interests in already existing knowledge. Science is inquiry incarnate, but government has now joined religion in regulating such inquiry and by consequence slowing it down or giving it more practical direction.

Thus the psychological solution could be effected by a cultural shift: easier adjustment of the organism to a slower gain in the increase of knowledge. As for the mentally unfit, this would be especially true. If stronger measures are needed, then deliberate cultural regression could be practiced. Hospitals for mental diseases ought to be constructed in the remote countryside, and approximate as near as possible to primitive conditions. Outdoor plumbing, wood fires for heating and cooking, crude accommodations, all designed to allow the readjustments to be slower. This is a possible solution, but it is not the ideal one.

For the ideal solution would combine the peace and serenity of conservatism with the excitement and vitality of progress, avoiding both the stalemate of repetition and the turmoil and insecurity of rapid change. There would be no longer any traditional ways of doing things but instead habits would be hooked up to an irregular rate of advance. Another biological adjustment would come into play: the tuneable homeostat of a servomechanism as the functioning model of the central nervous system (11, pp. 8–15).

So much for the psychological subject. As for the object, it would have to involve a better adjustment between institutions. No single institution would be allowed to run away with the others, but novelty would be provided by all. Cultural lags in institutional advancement would be studiously avoided and the proper institutional relations discovered and established. The elimination of human maladaptation depends upon the provision for a proper cultural environment, the ecological ideal upon the proper interdependence between the organism of the individual and the environment of the culture.

CHAPTER 6

THE STRESSED CONDITIONING OF
PSYCHOTICS

W E ARE now in a position to develop more fully the way in which an extension of existing techniques for the treatment of certain types of psychoses can be proposed. Recent experiences with the victims of "brainwashing" or of "coercive persuasion" suggest a more humane medical version for the mentally ill (1, 5, 7).

In many types of psychoses it is possible to discover a delusional system. Focused on some common obsession, as when the patient thinks he is Napoleon or the victim of persecution, there will be a general rearrangement of the data of all other experiences. The most completely systematized delusions are those peculiar to paranoia, but some found in paranoid schizophrenia are sufficiently developed to be called delusional systems. A delusional system is one which is internally consistent and externally in correspondence with the contradictories of some propositions which are supported by the relevant known facts.

Elsewhere it has been argued that a delusional system may represent the substitution of a private retention schema for a public one. Retention schemata have been defined already as sets of beliefs maintained in the unconscious, from where they may rise to the consciousness or otherwise influence behavior. In the case of the psychotic, the private retention schema is a delusional system, making considerable difficulty for the patient in his efforts to adapt to his immediate environment, while his substitution of his private retention schema for the public retention schema makes him a source of considerable difficulty for society. Therapy in both cases is urgently indicated.

In neurotics and normal individuals the interview dialogue may be sufficient to effect the desired substitution. Traditional examples are not wanting, as those who have read the Socratic dialogues are aware, and more recent instances may be adduced. However, in psychotics a more extended treatment is necessary.

The proposed therapy will consist in two separate stages. First, the delusional system will have to be dissipated, and then an appropriate substitution of the public retention schema properly effected. The first stage will be accomplished by experimental extinction, the second by stressed conditioning.

EXPERIMENTAL EXTINCTION OF DELUSIONAL SYSTEMS

Wolpe has shown that anxiety is a conditioned response, and moreover one which can be cancelled by aggressive assertiveness (9). In some psychotics also this may be the case. If so, experimental extinction may be effective.

In a patient with a delusional system it is possible to see the phenomenon of conditioning. Disturbed individuals were the ones most easily conditioned, and hence the ones by whom the delusional systems could be most firmly retained and recalled. The delusional system has been functioning as a public retention schema to a degree that makes the situation untenable for other individuals in the patient's immediate environment, hence the necessity for hospitalization.

The first desired effect is the dissociation of the delusional system from its security function as a public retention schema. This will have to consist in a process of experimental extinction. If every time the patient is reminded of his delusional system he is also noxiously stimulated, an experimental extinction of the delusional system can be accomplished.

Toward this end it will be necessary first by means of a series of interviews to isolate and abstract the delusional system. This can be done little by little and the parts then reassembled. The therapist will need to know the structure of the whole, but he will have a use for the parts. Most such structures take deductive form, they consist in a few axioms from which a larger number of theorems are drawn. In the therapeutic process of experimental extinction, more attention will be paid and more time given to the axioms than to the theorems.

The first part of the therapy, then, will consist in the process of experimental extinction applied to the axioms and theorems of the delusional system by means of repeated noxious stimulation. The selection of the proper agent to act as the conditioned stimulus will have to be a matter of trial and error. The noxious stimulus could be a distasteful liquid or gas, or a painful tactile stimulation. Something less severe than electroshock would be preferable, for several reasons. In the first place, the therapy will have to be repeated a number of times, and the patient will benefit more if conscious while habit patterns are being established. In the second place, electroshock is required for the positive next phase which is to consist of stressed conditioning.

The noxious stimulation is a negative substitute for the positive fact that the delusional system is losing its need reduction value as a security system. The procedure is the same followed in the inhibitory conditioned reflex. The propositions of the delusional system will have to be repeated to the patient by the therapist, to the accompaniment of the application of whatever noxious stimulus has been chosen for the purpose. This should have the effect on the patient of reducing his dependence upon the delusional system. A gradual diminution of belief in the system should be induced. After a sufficient number of such treatments, an occasional repetition of the noxious agent functioning as a conditioned stimulus alone should be adequate for reinforcement.

The second part of the therapy is as important as the first. Without stressed conditioning, there would have been little point in practicing experimental extinction. The patient deprived of his delusional system without further interference would be left to drift back into it. At the present time, in the treatment of psychotics by means of electroshock, the first stage of a two-stage process is employed but not the second, the channels are cleared without the necessary subsequent programming. It is not advisable to remove an undesirable program without substituting a desirable one. For there is always present the possibility of

"spontaneous recovery" (4, pp. 269–70) as evidenced by the phenomenon of "disinhibition," according to which a weak stimulus
will restore at least partially an experimentally extinguished reflex (4, pp. 272–73).

THE TECHNIQUE OF STRESSED CONDITIONING

The human individual's craving for knowledge is a cortical
need, having its origin in the animal need to approach and explore, called by Pavlov "the investigatory reflex" (6, p. 12). Curiosity is natural to man, and leads to belief. There is no such condition in the living individual as the absence of knowledge.
Ignorance is only another name for false knowledge, the holding
of beliefs which have no legitimate claim to truth. Memory traces
involve the activity of a receptacle; it is not possible permanently
to alter cortical tissue after a temporary process of excitation,
without recording a content. So long as there are engrams, there
will be beliefs.

Thus the controlled extinction of a delusional system requires
the prompt substitution of a public retention schema, which must
be ready to hand as a therapeutic device. An abstract formulation of a public retention schema must first be made up from a
knowledge of the basic values, since public retention schema is
only another name for the basic value system of a given society
(2, 3, 10). For the concise purposes of stressed conditioning, it
may be possible to generalize public retention schemata to a
more abstract form still, and to construct an universal public retention schema (UPRS), one which would be of service in almost
any society.

The UPRS would function as an emergency security system.
It would provide skeletal beliefs, a structure upon which more
native propositions could be hung. It would induce an active
orienting response with a degree of alertness which might indicate partial recovery.

There is, however, an important warning which must be pro-
claimed here. For it is at this point that the dangers of indoctrination make their appearance. A misguided therapist could do
incalculable harm were he alone to be assigned the task of select-
ing the contents of a public retention schema. The programming

of such a security system would have to carry social or institutional endorsement. It is too powerful an instrument to be left to one therapist to design.

A sample formulation of the UPRS is offered here, but with the greatest reservations, more specifically with the reminder that it is intended as nothing more than a tentative proposal. The UPRS consists in five propositions, which are as follows.

1) You are not alone. 2) We are all in the same world together. 3) If you can help him (her), he (she) will help you. 4) You can help him (her) while working alone. 5) You will think of nothing that you could not think for him (her).

The technique of employing the UPRS would be to slip it into place in bits, when possible, under stress. Each administration of electroshock would be followed by the enforced rote learning of the proposition, plus the repetition of the cumulative propositions to that date. Loud sounds and other intense stimuli such as bright lights and hot air offer facilitative support to the learning process in the sense of Skinner (8, pp. 16–17). Rest and recovery periods would be occasions for bits of illustrative action, such as doing small favors for nurses and attendants.

The two steps in the proposed therapy have been outlined separately, but they would have to be carried out together. The negative step of extinguishing the delusional system and the positive step of stressed conditioning would not take place on the same occasion but would be separated by not too much time. The procedure elsewhere described as transfer matching would here apply. The technique of experimental extinction would depend upon the exhaustion of the central nervous system as a result of its activity in response to repeated stimuli. The corresponding technique of stressed conditioning would depend equally upon rest and recovery occurring under the new circumstances brought about by the introduction of a fresh set of engrams.

The order of procedure would be that of primary reinforcement in the stressed conditioning we have been describing. It means following the conditioned stimulus (electroshock) with the unconditioned stimulus (knowledge). Secondary reinforcement and further stages will be furnished by the need-reduction provided by the stable conditions of the environing society. Thus it is important that as soon as appears advisable the patient be released from the hospital in the custody of his family. The feeling of security as a reinforcing agent for the beliefs which appear consistent with it and the actions which follow from it are important in establishing receptor-effector connections which it is hoped might endure.

CHAPTER 7

AN ILLUSTRATION OF
RETENTION SCHEMATA

I N THIS chapter, a theoretical position with respect to the nature of individual and social beliefs is illustrated by a set of interviews. It is necessary to begin with a statement of the theoretical position presented by means of definitions. However, nothing more final is intended by them than the formulation of an hypothesis. The report of the interviews is based on notes made at the time, supplanted from memory.

PRELIMINARY DEFINITIONS

Every individual has a security system consisting in a set of retention schemata. There is always a private retention schema and a public one. It will be recalled that by "private retention schema" is meant an unconscious set of experientially acquired and emotionally accepted and endorsed dispositional states. The private retention schema has a core of stability and a peripheral area of change; it requires and receives occasional reinforcement.

By "public retention schema," also as we have noted, is meant a system of social beliefs interpreted as rules of procedure whereby cognition is enabled on the one hand to apply its fundamental categories to sort out the data subsequently disclosed to sense experience and on the other to guide behavior.

The elements of the two schemata are rarely sorted. The private schema is peculiar to a given individual; the public schema common to all members of a given culture. The two schemata together constitute the beliefs of the individual. But there is no dead storage as in a computer; some of the beliefs must be revised from time to time as new information is received or new relations between bits of stored information detected.

The retention schemata are the results of continuing inquiry. When there is too litle or too much belief, a pathological situation results. To borrow an analogy, a liquid schema would not allow sufficient retention; a solid schema would not permit the slightest revision; a colloid or plastic schema would provide for both. When there is no belief except inquiry, even of a provisional nature, then there is no integrity, no order, no direction. When beliefs are entirely settled, then the consequent absoluteness makes for a rigidity which is non-adaptive.

The following experiment in mental health was undertaken to determine whether an overly rigid set of retention schemata could be broken and active inquiry restored.

THE SUBJECT

The subject was a German emigrant thirty-five years of age, educated at Heidelberg. He went into the furniture business in Dusseldorf, was maried to a Jewish girl and the father of one child. When the Nazis came to power, he emigrated with his family to New York where he succeeded in making a connection with a business similar to his former one. He was highly successful in business both in the country of his origin and in that of his adoption.

A healthy man of average size with a commanding presence, his attitude indicated an assumed superiority. He had little patience with disagreement. Preliminary conversations revealed an excellent memory and a considerable preference for the German intellectual background which he had acquired through education and experience. In the University he had been interested primarily in philosophy, and he continued to read philosophy for relaxation. Philosophy for him meant German or Greek philosophy exclusively, and he interpreted Greek philosophy altogether through German premises. He gave an impression of a powerful personality, without, however, its usual charm.

PRELIMINARY DISCUSSION

The subject was first encountered on a number of social occasions. He seemed unimpressed by a common philosophical interest but was willing and even sometimes eager to continue philosophical discussion, the discussion of which, however, was to inform the author, not enlighten the subject. Although an amateur, he regarded himself as more than the equal of all non-German professionals because he was German. He made it perfectly clear that he had nothing to learn from non-Germans.

All references to prominent British and American philosophers he accordingly dismissed with a shrug. The Germans were authorities, and everything else had been learned from them. Each reference to a particular non-German philosopher was traced by him immediately to an earlier German. Bertrand Russell, for instance, he said owed his metaphysics to Leibniz, his theory of knowledge to Meinong, and his logic to Frege. He knew that the American pragmatists, Peirce and James, derived their doctrine from Kant. This led to a discussion of Kant.

FIRST INTERVIEW

A. [*The author*] Have you read Hegel's criticisms of Kant?
S. [*The subject*] Hegel's points are more telling than those of others who have tried to demolish Kant's position. Nevertheless they can be answered. I don't think Hegel really understood Kant.
A. Kant is not easily understood, is he?
S. Not easily, no. I began his *Critique of Pure Reason* when a student, and I have not failed to read in it at least once every day since.
A. Do you think it that important?
S. I certainly do. It answers all the philosophical questions that had gone unanswered since the Greeks first raised them.
A. What about the friends of your undergraduate days, did they agree with you about the importance of Kant?
S. Not all, certainly. Many of them did, I should say a bare majority.

A. And friends made since then, your business acquaintances, for instance?

S. Very few of my friends share my enthusiasm for Kant or for philosophy, especially in America. With my business associates I have never had the time to discuss such matters. There was always business to be conducted. However, I could not help noticing that most Germans are Kantians whether they know it or not.

A. What do you make of the fact that Kant's parents were Scotch people who had settled in Germany? The family name was 'C-a-n-t' before Immanuel Kant changed the spelling.

S. Kant was born in Germany, and he gave the highest expression to the German spirit.

[*The private retention schema of the subject was constructed by employing the commonly accepted interpretation of Kant's* Critique. *There was no disposition to question it. The private and public retention schemata largely overlap; the subject is not psychotic.*]

A. What about the philosophers since Kant's time?

S. They could have saved their trouble. There has been no need for them.

A. Including the German philosophers?

S. Yes.

A. Husserl and Heidegger as well as Hegel?

S. Yes, they were not good Kantians.

A. But what about the problems of a philosophical nature which have occurred as a result of social events since Kant's day?

S. They could be solved by the proper application of Kant's system. We do not need new philosophers; originality in that field has been rendered superfluous. But we do need Kantians.

A. You mean qualified Kant scholars who could apply Kant's philosophy to contemporary situations?

S. Yes, that's what I mean.

A. Are there no problems that such an approach could not solve?

S. No.

A. Is it not possible that by getting outside of Kant's framework another and more insightful position might be undertaken, one which is perhaps more inclusive because of the new scientific knowledge which has developed in the last century and a half?

S.   There are other positions, certainly, but they are less inclusive rather than more. They resemble the pre-Kantian philosophers. It is not reasonable to behave as though Kant had not lived.

[*Since for the subject, all inquiry into philosophical fields had long been terminated, and the subject had been alerted as to the importance of reaffirming this, there was no point in pursuing the topic further at this time.*]

SECOND INTERVIEW

The second interview took place a week later. The subject seemed anxious to resume the discussion.

S.   The last time we talked you said nothing as to your own philosophical preferences. Are you a Kantian?

A.   That depends on what you mean by a Kantian. I think that Kant made a considerable contribution, but I am inclined to view his philosophy critically as he himself claimed to view all other philosophies. I think there are flaws in his work.

S.   There are no flaws. One either accepts Kant or one does not.

A.   Surely a man as intelligent as you has other interests. Even if we were to agree about Kant's importance there would be other things to talk about in the domain of ideas. What other intellectual interests do you have?

S.   Only one, mathematics. Particularly geometry—topology and the like.

A.   Was this in Heidelberg?

S.   It began in Heidelberg, but like my interest in Kant, it has persisted.

A.   You read mathematics now?

S.   Yes, when I can find the time. I try to keep up by subscribing to some of the journals.

A.   But surely learning mathematics by yourself is most difficult. This is a drill topic, like logic. One needs to have it explained, and then one needs to be rehearsed. There is a good deal of rote learning involved. Isn't the classroom the best place?

S. Of course it is. Especially if you plan to become a mathematician or to apply mathematics in a particular way, such as in mechanical engineering. I have found out, however, that there are two levels of understanding in mathematics. The one we have been talking about is for the man who wishes to operate it. He must be able to solve equations, derive formulas and the rest. For him there are few short cuts.

A. That's not your type of interest.

S. No, I am content with the second level of understanding. I want merely to grasp the concepts, not derive the formulas. It is possible to comprehend what the mathematicians are doing without being able to do it one's self. I can watch, for instance, while a geometrician solves what is for him at least a simple problem: finding the locus of the midpoints of a set of parallel chords of an ellipse; and I know perfectly well what he is doing, but I could not do it.

A. Is that satisfactory to you?

S. Yes. It has to be. Because that way I understand many of the more complex problems and their solutions. What I want most is to *understand* mathematics, not to do it.

[*The next question was a leading one. It would be no good if he could see where it was likely to take him. He was blinded, however, by the obscuring strength of his own dogmatism. He was an absolutist with respect to his own knowledge, and could not entertain the thought that it might contain contradictions.*]

A. You are familiar, of course, with the non-Euclidean geometries?

S. Indeed. Riemann and, to a somewhat lesser extent, Lobachevsky have made powerful and distinctive contributions.

A. I thought that the geometries of Riemann and Lobachevsky were equivalent. Riemannian geometry treats of convex surfaces while Lobachevskian deals with concave. Why do you say, "lesser extent"?

[*Riemann was German, Lobachevsky Russian.*]

S.   The Riemannian plane is the surface of a sphere, the Loba-
     chevskian plane the interior of a circle. In astronomy, it
     is only the convex surfaces of stars and planets which are
     available to observations by our instruments. The convex
     inner surfaces are not.

[*Since it appeared that there would be another interview, it
was deemed expedient to terminate the present one on this
note.*]

THIRD INTERVIEW

A.   I have been thinking that you are a superior sort of citizen
     to have your high quality of interests. There are not many
     business men who do.

S.   That is true. Making a living is one thing, and one's private
     life quite another. Considerable ingenuity is required in
     industry. I see no reason to sink below its requirements
     when I have leisure time.

A.   The tired banker in New York tries to find a sentimental
     music comedy in the evening.

S.   I know that, yes. Sometimes I have to go with him for busi-
     ness reasons, and when that is necessary I do not express
     any opinion contrary to his. I always pretend to find the
     musical entertaining. When I am alone it is different. I
     try to find a good performance of Bach or Mozart. Nothing
     later than the eighteenth century. I do not want to be en-
     tertained, as they say; I want to be enriched, I want to be
     elevated.

A.   Kant, Bach, non-Euclidean geometry—you lead a full life.

S.   Now or never.

A.   I would like to return to Kant for a moment.

S.   A pleasure.

A.   There was no non-Euclidean geometry in Kant's time. For
     Kant, geometry was Euclidean.

S.   Just so.

A.   But did not Kant go further than that?

S.   What do you mean?

A.   Correct me if I am wrong. It is my understanding that Kant asserted that Euclidean geometry is the form of the human mind.

S.   I don't think that Kant anywhere says it exactly like that, but it would follow from what he does say in the *Critique,* especially from B 120 and B 207.

A.   You know Kant well enough to remember the line numbers!

S.   I have an excellent visual memory. At least what you are saying is for Kant true of space; and since space is the outer form of the intuition and Euclidean geometry the only study of space, it would follow. But see also A 25 = B 40. In A 165 = B 206, Kant seems to admit that what geometry asserts belongs to the pure intuition. There are some relevant comments also in the *Dissertation.*

A.   Aren't you in trouble?

S.   How do you mean?

A.   Let me ask you this. Do you believe in non-Euclidean geometry as firmly as you do in Kant?

S.   I don't see that the acceptance of the one involves the rejection of the other. . . .

A.   What if it did?

S.   But it doesn't—it can't.

A.   Are you that sure? The parallel postulate which Euclid accepts Riemann rejects. In fact, Riemann accepts the contradictory of the parallel postulate, does he not?

S.   Yes.

A.   Well, then, if they are logically equivalent contradictories, how can the geometry which includes one of them only be the form of the human mind. What happens to the other? And if the form of the mind were to include both, would this not involve it in accepting a contradiction? And in that case, what would happen to logic?

[*At this point, the subject grew angry and appeared quite disturbed. He turned pale and began to breathe heavily. There was a long pause.*]

S.   Do you realize what you have done to me?

A.   No, what have I done?

S.   You have disturbed things that I had thought were settled for once and all. It is very upsetting and I resent it. Now I shall have to go home and rethink the whole problem over again. I should have known better than to argue with Americans!

CONCLUSIONS

When the subject was first encountered, he was secure in the solidity of his retention schemata. The pathological symptom was the ascendency of the private schema over the public schema, resulting in over-determined behavior (in this case the insistence on superior personal authority among non-German nationals) and the emotional acceptance of the public schema. But there were no conflicts. The chief feature of his private retention schema was the peculiar way in which it incorporated elements of the public schema. He was a German national; therefore in his view reliable knowledge issues from German authorities. Those he selected were from the fields of philosophy and mathematics. It was clear that he would not have considered objections emanating from other sources, as for instance from authorities who were members of other nationalities. To effect a breach in this solid front, a weakness had to be found in his own schemata and he perforce confronted with it. It would have to be an internal contradiction in the schemata.

The retention schemata are stored in a way which makes them available to releasing mechanisms. The weakest elements are capable of firing only vague inclinations to action, and consist in convictions quite easily disposed of, but the strongest have a compulsive character and carry an emotional charge. Strength of retention also means resistance to change. Retention schemata therefore must be disintegrated before fundamental inquiry can be reopened. Doubt is an interim affair, but it can replace belief in the service of inquiry. Belief is shaken only when contradictions or conflicts appear. Contradictions in retention schemata are found either between elements of the schemata and external fact or theory, or within the schemata. In the present case, the former would not have served; the latter was supplied.

REFERENCES

CHAPTER 1

1. Adrian, A. D.: *The Physical Background of Perception.* Oxford, Clarendon Press, 1947.
2. Bergson, H.: *Matter and Memory.* New York, Doubleday, 1959.
3. Bohm, D.: *Causality and Chance in Modern Physics.* New York, Van Nostrand, 1957.
4. Brazier, M. A. B. (ed.) : *The Central Nervous System and Behavior.* New York, Josiah Macy Jr. Foundation, 1959.
5. ———: *Ibid.* Jasper, H. H. *et al.* (ed.) : *Reticular Formation of the Brain.* Boston, Little Brown, 1958.
6. Farnsworth, P. R., and McNemar, Q. (ed.) : *Annual Review of Psychology,* Vol. 10. Palo Alto, Annual Reviews, Inc., 1959.
7. Feibleman, James K. *The Institutions of Society.* London, Allen and Unwin, 1956.
8. Halmos, P., and Iliffe, A. (ed.) : *Readings in General Psychology.* London, Routledge & Kegan Paul, 1959.
9. Harris, E. E.: *Nature, Mind and Modern Science.* New York, Macmillan, 1954.
10. Hilgard, E. R.: *Theories of Learning.* New York, Appleton-Century-Crofts, 1948.
11. Jeffress, L. A. (ed.) : *Cerebral Mechanisms in Behavior.* New York, Wiley, 1951.
12. Magoun, H. W.: *The Waking Brain.* Springfield, Thomas, 1958.
13. See e.g., Muller-Freienfels, R.: *The Evolution of Modern Psychology.* New Haven, Yale Univ. Press, 1935.
14. Murchison, C. (ed.) : *The Foundations of Experimental Psychology.* Worcester, Mass., Clark Univ. Press, 1929.
15. Osgood, C. E.: *Method and Theory in Experimental Psychology.* New York, Oxford Univ. Press, 1953.
16. Peirce, C. S.: *Collected Papers,* 8 Vols., Vol. I. §137–40. Cambridge, Harvard Univ. Press, 1931.

17. Piaget, J.: *Introduction A L'epistemologie Genetique*, 3 vols. Paris, Presses Universitaires de France, 1950.
18. ———: *The Construction of Reality in the Child*. New York, Basic Books, Inc., 1958.
19. Popper, K. R.: *The Logic of Scientific Discovery*. London, Hutchinson, 1959.
20. Russell, B.: *The Analysis of Mind*. London, Allen & Unwin, 1921.
21. Russell, W. R.: *Brain, Memory, Learning*. Oxford, Clarendon Press, 1959.
22. Sargant, W.: *Battle For the Mind*. New York, Doubleday, 1957.
23. Skinner, B. F.: *Verbal Behavior*. New York, Appleton-Century-Crofts, 1957.
24. Tinbergen, N.: *The Study of Instinct*. Oxford, Clarendon Press, 1951.
25. Tolman, E. C.: *Behavior and Psychological Man*, Ch. 4. Berkeley, Univ. of California Press, 1958. Cf. also Woodworth, R. S.: *Contemporary Schools of Psychology*. New York, Ronald Press, 1948.
26. See e.g., Troland, L. T.: *Motivational Psychology*. In *Psychologies of 1930*, p. 462, Murchison, C. (ed.). Worcester, Mass., Clark Univ. Press, 1930; and Walter, W. G.: *The Living Brain*, p. 43. London, Duckworth, 1957.
27. von Neumann, J.: *The Computer and the Brain*. New Haven, Yale Univ. Press, 1958.
28. Woodworth, R. S.: *Experimental Psychology*. New York, Holt, 1938.

CHAPTER 2

1. Anderson, B.: *Experientia*, 8:157 (1952).
2. Bartlett, Sir F. C.: *Remembering*. Cambridge Univ. Press, 1954.
3. Bradley, P. B.: The Central Action of Certain Drugs in Relation to the Reticular Formation of the Brain. In *Reticular Formation of the Brain*, Jasper, H. E. *et al.* (ed.). Boston, Little Brown, 1958.
4. Brazier, M. A. B.: Long-Persisting Electrical Traces in the Brain of Man and their Possible Relationship to Higher Nervous Activity. Moscow, *Moscow Colloquium on Electroencephalography of Higher Nervous Activity*, 1958.
5. Bruner, J. S.: Going Beyond the Information Given. In *Contem-*

porary Approaches to Cognition. University of Colorado Symp. Cambridge, Harvard Univ. Press, 1957.

6. Brunswik, E.: Scope and Aspects of the Cognitive Problem. In *Contemporary Approaches to Cognition.*

7. Critchley, M.: The Phenomenon of Tactile Inattention with Special Reference to Parietal Lesions. In *Brain, 72:538–561* (1949).

8. Festinger, L.: *A Theory of Cognitive Dissonance.* Evanston, Ill., Row Peterson, 1957.

9. Galambos, R.: *The Central Nervous System and Behavior.* Trans. of the First Conference. New York, Josiah Macy Jr. Foundation, 1959.

10. Gellhorn, E.: *Physiological Foundations of Neurology and Psychiatry.* Minneapolis, Univ. of Minnesota Press, 1956.

11. Gibson, J. J.: *The Perception of the Visual World.* Boston, Houghton Mifflin, 1950.

12. Granit, R.: *Receptors and Sensory Perception.* New Haven, Yale Univ. Press, 1955.

13. Head, Sir H.: *Studies in Neurology.* Oxford, Oxford Univ. Press, 1920.

14. Hobbes, T.: *Physica, iv:25.* OPP.ed. Molesworth. I:321.

15. Jackson, J. H.: *Selected Writings.* London, Hodder and Stoughton. 2 Vols. See in addition the references to Jackson and others in Fulton, J. F.: *Physiology of the Nervous System.* Pp. 386, 468–9, 481–2. New York, Oxford Univ. Press, 1951.

16. Jasper, H. H. *et al.:* Microelectrode Analysis of Cortical Cell Discharge During Avoidance Conditioning in the Monkey. Moscow, In *Moscow Colloquium on Electroencephalography of Higher Nervous Activity,* 1958.

17. Kant, I.: *Critique of Pure Reason, A:138* ff.

18. Kerr, D. I. B., and Hagbarth, K. E.: An Investigation of Olfactory Centrifugal Fiber System. *J. Neurophysiol., 18:362–74* (1955).

19. Levy-Bruhl, L.: *Les Fonctions Mentales Dans Les Societes Inferieurs.*

20. Livingston, R. B.: Central Control of Afferent Activity. *Reticular Formation of the Brain.* Boston, Little Brown, 1958.

21. Lorenza, K.: *King Solomon's Ring.* London, Methuen, 1952.

22. MacLean, P. D.: The Limbic System with Respect to Two Basic Life Principles. Brazier, M. A. B. (ed.): *The Central Nervous System and Behavior.* Trans. of Second Conference. New York, Josiah Macy Jr. Foundation, 1959.

23. McCulloch, W. S.: Modes of Functional Organization of the Cerebral Cortex. *Fed. Proc., 6:*488–52 (1947).

24. Magoun, H. W. The Ascending Reticular System and Wakefulness. Delafresnaye, J. F. (ed.) : *Brain Mechanisms and Consciousness.* Oxford, Blackwell, 1954.

25. ———: *The Waking Brain.* Springfield, Thomas, 1958.

26. Meyer, J. S.: Studies of Cerebral Circulation in Brain Injury: IV: Ischemia and Hypoxemia of the Brain Stem and Respiratory Center. *EEG Clin. Neurophysiol., 1:*83–100 (1957).

27. Mill, J. S.: *Examination of Sir William Hamilton's Philosophy, 1:*14. Boston, 1865.

28. Peele, T. L.: *The Neuroanatomical Basis for Clinical Neurology.* New York, McGraw-Hill, 1954.

29. Ransom, S. W., Fisher, C., and Ingram, W. R.: Hypothalamic Regulation of Temperature in the Monkey. *A.M.A. Arch. Neurol. Psychiat., 38:*445–66 (1937).

30. Schiller, C. H. (ed.) : *Instinctive Behavior.* London, Methuen, 1957.

31. Sherrington, C.: *The Integrative Action of the Nervous System.* New York, Scribner, 1906.

32. Schwartzbaum, J. S.: Changes in Reinforcing Properties of Stimuli following Ablation of the Amygdaloid Complex in Monkeys. *J. Comp. Physiol.,* (In Press).

33. Tinbergen, N.: *The Herring Gull's World.* London, Collins, 1953.

34. ———: *The Study of Instinct.* Oxford, Oxford University Press, 1951.

35. Tolman, E. C.: *Behavior and Psychological Man.* Berkeley and Los Angeles, Univ. of California Press, 1958.

36. Walter, W. G.: A Statistical Approach to the Theory of Conditioning. Moscow, *Moscow Colloquium on Electroencephalography of Higher Nervous Activity,* 1958.

CHAPTER 3

1. Festinger, L.: *A Theory of Cognitive Dissonance.* Evanston, Ill., Row Peterson, 1957.

2. Goldstein, K.: *The Organism: A Holistic Approach to Biology Derived from Pathological Data in Man.* New York, American Book Co., 1939.

3. Pribram, K. H.: A Review of Theory in Physiological Psychology.

Farnsworth, P. R., and McNemar, Q. (ed.) : *Annual Review of Psychology*. Palo Alto, Annual Reviews, Inc., 1960.
4. Sargant, W.: *Battle for the Mind*. New York, Doubleday, 1957.

CHAPTER 4

1. Arieti, S.: *Interpretation of Schizophrenia*. New York, Brunner, 1955.
2. Ashby, W. R.: The Mechanism of Habituation. *Mechanization of Thought Processes*, Vol. I, pp. 95–113. London, Her Majesty's Stationery Office, 1959. See also the comments of W. Grey Walter, pp. 115–16.
3. Dell, P. C.: Humoral Effects on the Brain Stem Reticular Formation. Jasper, H. H., and others (ed.) : *Reticular Formation of the Brain*. Boston, Little Brown, 1958.
4. Deutsch, J. A.: A New Type of Behavior Theory. *The Brit. J. Psychol.*, *44*:304–17 (1953).
5. Dobzhansky, T.: *Evolution, Genetics and Man*. New York, Wiley, 1955. Wallace, B., and Dobzhansky, T.: *Radiation, Genes and Man*. New York, Holt, 1959.
6. Gellhorn, E.: *Physiological Foundations of Neurology and Psychiatry*. Minneapolis, Univ. of Minnesota Press, 1953.
7. Gerard, R. W.: Brains and Behavior. Spuhler, J. N. (ed.) : *The Evolution of Man's Capacity for Culture*.
8. Kolmogorov, A. N.: *Foundations of the Theory of Probability*. New York, Chelsea, 1956.
9. Livingston, R. B.: Central Control of Afferent Activity. Jasper, H. H. and others (ed.) : *Reticular Formation of the Brain*. Boston, Little Brown, 1958.
10. MacLean, P. D.: The Limbic System with Respect to Two Basic Life Principles. *The Central Nervous System and Behavior*. Trans. of the Second Conference. Brazier, M. A. B. (ed.) New York, Josiah Macy Jr. Foundation, 1959.
11. Magoun, H. W.: *The Waking Brain*. Springfield, Thomas, 1958.
12. Magoun, H. W., Darling, L., and Prost, J.: The Evolution of Man's Brain. Brazier, M. A. B. (ed.) : *The Central Nervous System and Behavior*. New York, Josiah Macy Jr. Foundation, 1960.
13. Musil, R.: *The Man Without Qualities*. London, Secker and Warburg, 1953.
14. Opler, M. K. (ed.) : *Culture and Mental Health*. New York, Macmillan, 1959.

15. Piaget, J.: *The Psychology of Intelligence.* London, Routledge and Kegan Paul, 1951.
16. Rosser, J. B., and Turquette, A. R.: *Many-valued Logics.* Amsterdam, North Holland Pub. Co., 1952.
17. Russell, W. R.: *Brain, Memory, Learning.* Oxford, Clarendon Press, 1959.
18. von Neumann, J.: The General and Logical Theory of Automata. Jeffress, L. A. (ed.) : *Cerebral Mechanisms in Behavior.* New York, The Hixon Symposium, 1951.
19. Walter, W. G.: A Statistical Approach to the Theory of Conditioning. *Moscow Colloquium on Electroencephalography of Higher Nervous Activity.* Jasper, H. H., and Smirnov, G. D. (ed.) : Montreal, *EEG Journal,* 1960.
20. Washburn, S. L.: Tools and Human Evolution. *Scientific American, 203*:63–75 (1960).

CHAPTER 5

1. Adrian, E. D.: *The Physical Background of Perception.* Oxford, Clarendon Press, 1947.
2. Bartlett, Sir F. C.: *Remembering.* Cambridge, Cambridge Univ. Press, 1954.
3. See, for instance, Fulton, J. F.: *Physiology of the Nervous System. Passim.* New York, Oxford Univ. Press, 1951.
4. Gellhorn, E.: *Physiological Foundations of Neurology and Psychiatry.* Minneapolis, Univ. of Minnesota Press, 1956, p. 425. See in this connection also, Chapter 17.
5. Gibson, J. J.: *Perception of the Visual World.* Boston, Houghton Mifflin, 1950.
6. Janet, P.: *Major Symptoms of Hysteria.* New York, Macmillan. 1920.
7. Jasper, H. H. *et al.* (ed.) : *Reticular Formation of the Brain.* Henry Ford Hospital International Symposium. Boston, Little Brown, 1958.
8. Senator Pat McNamara reporting for a Senate Investigating Subcommittee on Problems of the Aged and Aging, quoted in *The New York Times,* September 18, 1960.
9. Nelson, R., and Gellhorn, E.: The Influence of Age and Functional Neuropsychiatric Disorders on Sympathetic and Parasympathetic Functions. *J. Psychosomat. Research, 3*:12–26 (1958). Gellhorn, E.: *Physio. Found.,* pp. 429–488.

10. Poche, Irwin, in *Punch* (Monthly journal of the New Orleans Athletic Club).

11. Pribram, K. H.: A Review of Theories in Physiological Psychology. Farnsworth, P. R., and McNemar, Q. (ed.) : *Annual Review of Psychology.* Palo Alto, Cal., Annual Reviews, Inc., 1960.

12. Tolman, E. C.: *Behavior and Psychological Man.* Berkeley, Univ. of California Press, 1958.

13. Walter, W. G.: A Statistical Approach to the Theory of Conditioning. Jasper, H. H., and Smirnov, G. D.: *The Moscow Colloquium on Electroencephalography of Higher Nervous Activity.* Montreal, Canada, *EEG Journal,* 1960.

CHAPTER 6

1. Biderman, A. D., and Zimmer, H. (ed.) : *The Manipulation of Human Behavior.* New York, Wiley, 1961.

2. Clough, S. B.: *The Basic Values of Western Civilization.* New York, Columbia Univ. Press, 1961.

3. Feibleman, James K.: Toward the Analysis of the Basic Value System. *American Anthropologist, 56:421–432* (1954).

4. Hull, C. L.: *Principles of Behavior.* New York, Appleton-Century, 1943.

5. Lifton, R.: *Thought Reform and the Psychology of Totalism.* New York, Norton, 1961.

6. Pavlov, I. P.: *Conditioned Reflexes.* G. V. Anrep Trans. New York, Dover, 1960.

7. Schein, E., with Schneider, I., and Barker, C. H.: *Coercive Persuasion.* New York, Norton, 1961.

8. Skinner, B. F.: *The Behavior of Organisms.* New York, Appleton-Century-Crofts, 1938.

9. Wolpe, J.: *Psychotherapy by Reciprocal Inhibition.* Stanford, Stanford Univ. Press, 1958.

10. Van Zandt, R.: *The Metaphysical Foundations of American History.* The Hague, Mouton & Co., 1959.

CHAPTER 7

Ellis, Albert: A Homosexual Treated with Rational Psychotherapy. *J. Clin. Psychol., XV:338–343* (1959).

INDEX OF PROPER NAMES

INDEX OF TOPICS